Steidl
Fall/Winter 2019/2020

Cover drawings by Paloma Tarrio Alves / Steidl

"The Ballad of Sexual Dependency" made Nan Goldin famous. For years, the photographic artist and New York barmaid followed friends and chance acquaintances with her camera, photographing them in wild, vulnerable, desperate moments. The intensely colored images, which were published as a book in 1986, create a sense of romanticized realism, showing people lazily masturbating, light-headed couples shortly before sex, drug addicts, seriously ill AIDS victims, fragile existences. At one point she appears in an image herself with a bruised eye after her lover hit her. Goldin's touching figures appear to be more addicted to than really cut out for life.

Now, however, the 65-year-old artist has taken matters firmly into her own hands. She is battling Purdue Pharma, the American company that uses aggressive advertising to promote opioids as pain relief for the people of the USA, despite more than 200,000 people supposedly having died as a result of using them. The company, which is up in court in the US, belongs to members of the Sackler industrial dynasty, and the Sacklers have for many years been patrons of cultural institutions. These include New York's Metropolitan and Guggenheim Museums, as well as the Louvre, London's Tate Gallery and the Jewish Museum in Berlin. Now Goldin and her fellow campaigners are calling for museums to stop taking what she terms "blood money" from the Sacklers.

The photographer knows what she's talking about: she herself was once addicted to heroin, and then five years ago she succumbed to the painkiller OxyContin, which had been prescribed to her after an operation. In interviews

Nan Goldin

in the Fight against Blood Money

she recalls the feeling of warmth that the drug rush gave her, but also lonely days in darkened bedrooms, and ultimately the risk of death from the high doses she obtained illegally.

The money for this came from sales of her art to some of the museums of which the Sacklers were patrons. Since getting clean, Goldin has celebrated a revival—no longer as a chronicler of nightlife, but rather as an activist by day: scraps of paper fluttered down the spiral staircase of the Guggenheim Museum in New York, reminiscent of torn prescriptions, while at Washington's Smithsonian Institution, protesters lay on the ground as if they were dead.

The pressure is working. The Guggenheim Museum is no longer willing to accept Sackler dollars, and last week London's National Portrait Gallery rejected a donation from the Sacklers to the tune of one million pounds. The Tate no longer wants any money from the family either; indeed the word from South London is that the gallery actually returned a donation as long ago as last year. The Sacklers emphasize that by no means all its family members who are active patrons gained their wealth through opioids; meanwhile the Sacklers have for their part decided to make no further donations in London.

Britain's museums are reacting with mixed feelings to Goldin's campaign. Ultimately, the public purse is providing less and less funding for art and the Sackler empire is not notorious for getting involved too much on the content side. Art historians fear that they may have no funding left if campaigns against patrons like the Sacklers and indeed oil corporation BP prove successful.

Nan Goldin sees herself as a spokesperson for victims and takes a moral stance. This hasn't always been the case. In the past she has sharply rejected critics who claimed she should have greater awareness of her social responsibility as an artist and accused her of making heroin chic with her intimate insights into the drug scene. In the 1990s the fashion industry picked up on Goldin's visual style and likewise flirted with drug addiction. Later, the taboo on showing very private images to the masses was also ignored in social media—here again Goldin can be considered a pioneer.

KIA VAHLAND

„Die Ballade von der sexuellen Abhängigkeit" hat Nan Goldin berühmt gemacht. Über Jahre begleitete die Fotokünstlerin und New Yorker Barfrau Freunde und Zufallsbekanntschaften mit der Kamera, fotografierte sie in wilden, verletzlichen, verzweifelten Momenten. Die farbstarken Bilder, 1986 als Buch veröffentlicht, zeigen in romantisierendem Realismus müde Masturbierende, benommene Pärchen kurz vor dem Sex, Drogensüchtige, schwer Aidskranke, fragile Existenzen. Sie selbst tritt einmal mit blutunterlaufenem Auge ins Bild, ihr Liebhaber hatte sie zusammengeschlagen. Eher lebenssüchtig als lebenstüchtig wirken Goldins anrührende Figuren zumeist.

Nun aber hat die 65-jährige Künstlerin das Heft des Handelns in die Hand genommen. Sie bekämpft Purdue Pharma, die Firma, die in den USA mit aggressiver Werbung Opioide als Schmerzmittel unter das Volk brachte, woraufhin mehr als 200 000 Menschen gestorben sein sollen. Die Firma, die in den USA vor Gericht steht, gehört Mitgliedern der Industriellenfamilie Sackler. Und die Sacklers fördern seit Langem Kultureinrichtungen. Darunter sind das New Yorker Metropolitan und das Guggenheim Museum, der Louvre, die Londoner Tate Gallery und das Jüdische Museum in Berlin. Goldin und ihre Mitstreiter verlangen, dass Museen kein, wie sie sagen, „Blutgeld" von den Sacklers mehr annehmen.

Die Fotografin weiß, wovon sie spricht: Früher war sie einmal abhängig von Heroin; vor fünf Jahren verfiel sie dann dem Schmerzmittel Oxycontin, das ihr nach einer Operation verschrieben worden war. Sie erinnert sich in Interviews an ein Gefühl der Wärme, in das der Medikamen-

Nan Goldin

Fotokünstlerin
im Kampf gegen
„Blutgeld"

tenrausch sie getaucht habe, aber auch an einsame Tage in abgedunkelten Schlafzimmern und schließlich an Todesgefahr durch die hohen Dosen, die sie sich illegal verschaffte.

Das Geld dafür gewann sie aus dem Verkauf ihrer Kunst an einige der Museen, welche die Sacklers fördern. Seit ihrem Entzug feiert Goldin ein Revival – nicht mehr als Chronistin des Nachtlebens, sondern als Aktivistin bei Tage: Im gewundenen Treppenhaus des Guggenheim Museum in New York flatterten Papierschnipsel herab, die an zerrissene Rezepte erinnern; in der Washingtoner Smithsonian

Institution legten die Protestierenden sich wie tot auf den Boden.

Der Druck wirkt. Das Guggenheim Museum will keine Sackler-Dollar mehr annehmen. Und in London hat die National Portrait Gallery vergangene Woche eine Spende der Sacklers in Höhe von einer Million Pfund abgelehnt, die Tate Gallery mag auch kein Geld der Familie mehr akzeptieren und aus der South London Gallery war zu hören, das Haus habe bereits im vergangenen Jahr eine Spende zurückgegeben. Die Sacklers betonen, dass keineswegs alle mäzenatisch tätigen Familienmitglieder mit Opioiden reich geworden seien. Sie verzichten in London jetzt ihrerseits auf weitere Spenden.

Britische Museumsleute reagieren mit gemischten Gefühlen auf Goldins Kampagne. Schließlich gibt die öffentliche Hand immer weniger Geld für Kunst aus, und das Sackler-Imperium ist nicht berüchtigt dafür, sich inhaltlich allzu sehr einzumischen. Die Kunsthistoriker fürchten, bald gar keine Mittel mehr zu haben, wenn Kampagnen gegen Förderer wie etwa auch den Ölkonzern BP Erfolg haben.

Nan Goldin sieht sich als Opfervertreterin, sie argumentiert moralisch. Das war nicht immer so. Früher wies sie Kritiker scharf zurück, die von ihr als Künstlerin soziales Verantwortungsbewusstsein verlangten und ihr vorwarfen, mit ihren intimen Einblicken in die Drogenszene Heroin schick zu machen. In den 90er-Jahren hatte die Modeindustrie Goldins Optik aufgegriffen und ebenfalls mit Drogensucht kokettiert. Später dann fiel in den sozialen Medien auch das Tabu, massenhaft sehr private Bilder zu zeigen. Auch dafür kann Goldin als eine der Vorreiterinnen gelten.   KIA VAHLAND

FOTO: GETTY

This catalogue is not for sale · © 2019 for this publication by Steidl Publishers, Germany · © 2019 for the images by the artists · © 2019 for the texts by the authors
Production and printing by Steidl, Düstere Str. 4, 37073 Göttingen, Germany · Phone +49 551 49 60 60 · Fax +49 551 49 60 649 · mail@steidl.de · steidl.de
All rights reserved · Printed in Germany by Steidl · ISBN 978-3-95829-641-1

4

Contents

Steidl

Düstere Str. 4
37073 Göttingen
Germany
T +49 551 4 960 60
F +49 551 4 960 649
E mail@steidl.de
www.steidl.de

Sales

Matthias Wegener
T +49 551 4 960 616
F +49 551 4 960 649
E mwegener@steidl.de

Susanne Schmidt
T +49 551 4 960 612
F +49 551 4 960 649
E sschmidt@steidl.de

Submissions

Holger Feroudj
E holger@steidl.de

Catalogue / Editorial

Holger Feroudj
T +49 551 49060 621
E holger@steidl.de

Export Management / Shipping

Jan Menkens
T +49 551 4 960 618
F +49 551 4 960 617
E jmenkens@steidl.de

Production

Bernard Fischer
T +49 551 4 960 633
F +49 551 4 960 634
E bfischer@steidl.de

Public Relations / Press

Claudia Glenewinkel
T +49 551 4 960 650
F +49 551 4 960 644
E cglenewinkel@steidl.de

Germany, Austria and Switzerland

Steidl Verlag
Claudia Glenewinkel
Düstere Str. 4
37073 Göttingen
Germany
T +49 551 4 960 650
F +49 551 4 960 644
E presse@steidl.de

USA and Canada

Monika Condrea
91 Saratoga Ave.
Brooklyn, NY 11233
USA
T +1 646 226 6828
E monika.condrea@gmail.com

France

Patrick Remy
22, Place Charles Fillion
75017 Paris
France
T +33 1 42 632 167
E patremy2@wanadoo.fr

All other territories

Steidl Verlag
Claudia Glenewinkel
Düstere Str. 4
37073 Göttingen
Germany
T +49 551 4 960 650
F +49 551 4 960 644
E presse@steidl.de

Edition 7L Paris

Caroline Lebar
7, rue de Lille
75007 Paris
France
T +33 1 44 502 200
F +33 1 44 502 205
E caroline.lebar@karllagerfeld.com

Steidl Dangin Publishers

Box Ltd.
Attn.: Marion Liang
267 Douglass Street
Brooklyn, NY 11217
USA
T +1 212 965 9555
F +1 212 965 9555
E info@boxstudios.com

Steidl David Zwirner

Doro Globus
525 West 19th Street
New York, NY 10011
T +1 212 7 272 070
F +1 212 7 272 072
E doro@davidzwirner.com
www.davidzwirner.com

Steidl Miles

Peter Miles Studio
650 East 6th Street, Apt. 1
New York, NY 10009
T +1 212 3 587 991
E email@petermilesstudio.com

Verlag

Steidl GmbH & Co. OHG
Düstere Straße 4
37073 Göttingen
T +49 551 4 960 60
F +49 551 4 960 649
E mail@steidl.de
steidl.de

Vertrieb

Matthias Wegener
T +49 551 4 960 616
F +49 551 4 960 649
E mwegener@steidl.de

Susanne Schmidt
T +49 551 4 960 612
F +49 551 4 960 649
E sschmidt@steidl.de

Auslieferungen

Deutschland

Steidl
Düstere Str. 4
37073 Göttingen
T +49 551 49 60 60
F +49 551 49 60 49
E bestellung@steidl.de

Lieferanschrift
Steidl
Anna-Vandenhoek-Ring 17
37081 Göttingen

Österreich

Mohr-Morawa
Sulzengasse 2
A-1232 Wien
T +43 1 680 140
F +43 1 687 130
E bestellung@mohrmorawa.at

Schweiz

AVA
Centralweg 16
CH-8910 Affoltern am Albis
T +41 44 7 624 200
F +41 44 7 624 210
E avainfo@ava.ch

Außendienst

Deutschland

Schleswig-Holstein, Hamburg, Bremen, Niedersachsen

Bodo Föhr Verlagsvertretungen
Lattenkamp 90
22299 Hamburg
T +49 40 51493667
F +49 40 51493666
E bodofoehr@freenet.de

Berlin, Mecklenburg-Vorpommern, Brandenburg

Vera Grambow
Liselotte-Herrmann-Straße 2
10407 Berlin
T +49 30 40 048 583
F +49 30 4 212 246
E berliner-verlagsvertretungen
   @t-online.de

Sachsen-Anhalt, Sachsen, Thüringen

Thomas Kilian
Vor dem Riedtor 11
99310 Arnstadt
T +49 362 85 493 310
F +49 362 85 493 310
E thomas.c.kilian@web.de

Nordrhein-Westfalen Hessen, Rheinland-Pfalz, Saarland, Luxemburg

Benedikt Geulen
Meertal 122
41464 Neuss
T +49 2131 1 255 990
F +49 2131 1 257 944
E benedikt.geulen@t-online.de

Ulrike Hölzemann
Dornseiferstr. 67
57223 Kreuztal
T +49 2732 55 83 44
F +49 2732 55 83 45
E u.hoelzemann@buerofuerbuecher.de

Baden-Württemberg

Tilmann Eberhardt
Verlagsvertretungen
Ludwigstr. 93
70197 Stuttgart
T +49 711 615 28 20
F +49 711 615 31 01
E Tilmann.Eberhardt@gmail.com

Bayern

Günter Schubert
Brunnenstraße 20a
85598 Baldham
T +49 8106 377 23 97
F +49 8106 377 23 98
E guenterschubert@t-online.de

Österreich

Jürgen Sieberer
Arnikaweg 79/4
1220 Wien
T +43 285 45 22
F +43 285 45 22
E juergen.sieberer@mohrmorawa.at

Günter Thiel
Reuharting 11
4652 Steinerkirchen
T +43 664 3 912 835
F +43 664 773 912 835
E guenter.thiel@mohrmorawa.at

Schweiz

Giovanni Ravasio
Verlagsvertretungen
Klosbachstr. 33
CH-8032 Zürich
T +41 44 260 61 31
F +41 44 260 61 32
E g.ravasio@bluewin.ch

Artbook | D.A.P.
75 Broad Street
Suite 630
New York, N.Y. 10004
USA
T +1 212 627 1999
F +1 212 627 9484
E orders@dapinc.com
www.artbook.com

Trade Sales Representatives

USA — West Coast / Southwest
Ellen Towell
Karel/Dutton Group
3145 Geary Blvd. #619
San Francisco CA 94118
T +1 415-668-0829
F +1 415-668-2463
E hkarel@comcast.net

Lise Solomon
Albany CA
T +1 510-528-0579
F +1 510-900-1088
E lise.solomon@sonic.net

Dory Dutton
Karel/Dutton Group
Corrales NM
T +1 818-269-4882
F +1 480-247-5158
E dory.dutton
   @valleyvilleemail.com

Southern California
Mark O'Neal
T + 1 562 587 0956
F + 1 877 847 1619
E oneal.mark@gmail.com

Midwest
Stu Abraham
Minneapolis MN
T +1 952-927-7920
F +1 952-927-8089
E stu@aabookreps.com

John Mesjak
Sycamore IL 60178
T +1 815-899-0079
F +1 815-261-4114
E john@aabookreps.com
Sandra Law
T + 1 630 352 8640
F + 1 952 927 8089
E. sandra@aabookreps.com

Emily Johnson
St. Paul MN
T +1 952 927 7920
F +1 952 927 8089
E emily@aabookreps.com

Mid-South / Southeast
Bill McClung / Terri McClung
Spring Branch TX
T +1 888-813-6563
F +1 888-311-8932
E bmcclung@ix.netcom.com
E tmcclung@ix.netcom.com

New England / Southeast
Zachary Goss
T + 1 774 644 7374
E zgoss@dapinc.com

Mark Pearson
CT, RI, MA, NH, VT, ME,
VA, NC, SC, GA, FL
T 617-480-1709
F 800-478-3128
E mpearson@dapinc.com

Mid-Atlantic
Chesapeake & Hudson, Inc.
Michael Gourley, Bill Hoar, Janine
Jensen, Steve Straw, Ted Wedel
T +1 800-231-4469
F +1 800-307-5163
E office@cheshud.com

National Accounts
Artbook | D.A.P.
Jane Brown
Los Angeles CA
T +1 323-969-8985
F +1 818-243-4676
E jbrown@dapinc.com

Gift Reps

Aesthetic Movement
New York & Mid-Atlantic
Gus Anagnopoulos
T +1 718-797-5750
F +1 718-797-4944
E gus@aestheticmovement.com

Aesthetic Movement
Chicago & Midwest
Alison Grant
T +1 773-951-8754
F +1 773-435-6691
E ali@aestheticmovement.com

Aesthetic Movement
Atlanta & Southern States
Laura Jane Turner
T +1 404-749-5005
F +1 404-521-4372
E laura@aestheticmovement.com

Artbook | Gift
Los Angeles & West Coast
Tricia Gabriel
T +1 323-969-8985
F +1 323-662-7896
E triciagabriel@gmail.com

Canada

Ampersand Inc.
Toronto On & East Coast
Saffron Beckwith
T +1 416-703-0666
F +1 866-849-3819
E saffronb@ampersandinc.ca

Ampersand Inc.
Vancouver BC & West Coast
Ali Hewitt
T +1 604-448-7165
F +1 888-323-7118
E cherylf@ampersandinc.ca

Ampersand Inc.
Ottawa & Quebec
Jenny Enriquez
T +1 416-703-0666
F +1 866-849-3819
E jennye@ampersandinc.ca

Paris Sales Office

Patrick Remy
22, Place Charles Fillion
75017 Paris
France
T +33 1 42 632 167
F +33 1 42 265 518
E patremy2@wanadoo.fr

For publications in English:

Interart S.A.R.L.
1, rue de l'Est
75020 Paris
T +33 1 43 493 660
F +33 1 43 494 122
E info@interart.fr

Responsable distribution:
Laurence H'Limi
E laurence@interart.fr

Responsable diffusion:
Pierre Samoyault
E pierre@interart.fr

Représentants:
Blanche Pilven
E blanche@interart.fr

Emerick Charpentier
E emerick@interart.fr

Margot Rietsch
E margot@interart.fr

Assistante commerciale:
Marylaure Perre
E marylaure@interart.fr

Service commande:
E commercial@interart.fr
www.dilicom.net

For publications in French:

SODIS
128, avenue du Maréchal-de-Lattre-
de-Tassigny
BP 142
77400 Lagny

Traitement des commandes
Responsable: Maeva Knisy
T +33 1 60 079 554

Identification DILICOM transmission:
SODILA (les commandes codifiées
transmises par DILICOM sont assurées du
traitement le plus rapide)
T +33 1 60 0 78 299
F +33 1 64 303 227

Relations clientèle
Chef de service: Pierrette Kimmel
T +33 1 60 078 201
F +33 1 64 308 805
E pierrette.kimmel@sodis.fr

Assistante Réclamations: Vic Mojasevic
T +33 1 60 078 633
F +33 1 64 308 806
E slavica.mojasevic@sodis.fr

Head Office / Export Sales Department: Thames & Hudson Ltd.

181a High Holborn
London WC1V 7QX
T +44 20 78 455 000
F +44 20 78 455 050
Sales and Marketing Department:
F +44 20 78 455 055
E sales@thameshudson.co.uk
E export@thameshudson.co.uk

UK

Ben Gutcher
Head of UK Sales
T 020 7845 5000
E b.gutcher@thameshudson.co.uk

Christian Frederking
Group Sales Director
E c.frederking@thameshudson.co.uk

Andrius Juknys
Head of Distributed books
T 020 7845 5000
F 020 7845 5055
E a.juknys@thameshudson.co.uk

Mark Garland
Manager, Distributed Books
T 020 7845 5000
F 020 7845 5055
E m.garland@thameshudson.co.uk

Ellen Morris
Distributed Sales Coordinator
T 020 7845 5000
F 020 7845 5055
E e.morris@thameshudson.co.uk

Dawn Shield
T 020 7845 5000
E d.shield@thameshudson.co.uk
London

David Howson
T 020 7845 5000
E d.howson@thameshudson.co.uk
London & South East

Karim White
T 07740 768 900
E k.white@thameshudson.co.uk
Northern England, Scotland & Ireland

Mike Lapworth
T 07745 304 088
E mikelapworth@sky.com
The Midlands & East Anglia

Ian Tripp
T 07970 450 162
E iantripp@ymail.com
Wales & Southwestern Counties

Trade: Thames & Hudson (Distributors) Ltd. (distribution and accounts)

Littlehampton Book Services
Faraday Close
Durrington, Worthing
West Sussex BN13 3RB
United Kingdom
T +44 190 382 8501

Key Accounts

Gethyn Jordan
T 020 7845 5000
E g.jordan@thameshudson.co.uk

Michelle Strickland
T 020 7845 5000
E m.strickland@thameshudson.co.uk

Alice Corrigan
T 020 7845 5028
E a.corrigan@thameshudson.co.uk

Gift

Jamie Denton
T 07765 403 182
E jamesdenton778@btinternet.com
South, Southeastern Counties/Gift

Victoria Hutton
T 07899 941 010
E victoriahuttonbooks@yahoo.co.uk
London/Gift

Colin MacLeod
T 07710 852 197
E colinmacleodsw@gmail.com
Wales & Southwestern Counties/Gift

Jill Macleod
T 07885 720 175
E colinmacleodsw@gmail.com
Wales & Southwestern Counties/Gift

For all other UK enquiries please contact:
Ellen McDermot
T 020 7845 5000
E sales@thameshudson.co.uk

Europe

Austria, Germany, Switzerland
Michael Klein
T +49 931 17405
E mi-klein@t-online.de

Belgium and Luxembourg

Alexandra Levy
Export Sales Department
Thames & Hudson Ltd
E a.levy@thameshudson.co.uk

Netherlands

Van Ditmar b.v.
Bas van der Zee
E th@vanditmar.audax.nl

Eastern Europe

Sara Ticci
T +44 7952 919 866
E s.ticci@thameshudson.co.uk

Eastern Mediterranean, Bulgaria, Romania

Stephen Embrey
T +44 7952 919 866
E s.embrey@thameshudson.co.uk

France

Interart S.A.R.L.
T (1) 43 49 36 60
E commercial@interart.fr

Spain, Italy and Portugal

Natasha Ffrench
Export Sales Department
Thames & Hudson Ltd
E n.ffrench@thameshudson.co.uk

Scandinavia, Baltic States, Russia and the CIS

Per Burell
T +46 (0) 70 725 1203
E p.burell@thameshudson.co.uk

The Near & Middle East

Middle East incl. Egypt
Stephen Embrey
T +44 7952 919 866
E s.embrey@thameshudson.co.uk

Africa

Africa (excluding South)
Ian Bartley
Export Sales Department
Thames & Hudson Ltd
E i.bartley@thameshudson.co.uk

South Africa, Swaziland, Lesotho, Namibia and Botswana

Jonathan Ball Publishers
66 Mimetes Road
Denver
Johannesburg, 2094
South Africa
www.jonathanball.co.za

Sales manager: Keryn Colyn
Tel: +27 (0) 11 601 8033
Email: Keryn.Colyn@Jonathanball.co.za

Asia and Far East

North East Asia
Thames & Hudson Asia
Units B&D 17/F
Gee Chang ong Centre
65 Wong Chuk Hang Road
Aberdeen
Hong Kong
T+852 2 553 9289
F+852 2 554 2912

Philip Tsang
Managing Director
E philip_tsang@asiapubs.com.hk

China, Hong Kong, Macau and Korea

Zita Chan
Regional Sales Manager
E zita_chan@asiapubs.com.hk

Taiwan

Helen Lee
E helen_lee@asiapubs.com.hk

Japan

Philip Tsang
E philip_tsang@asiapubs.com.hk

South East Asia

APD Singapore PTE Ltd
52 Genting Lane
#06-05, Ruby Land Complex
Singapore 349560
T (65) 6749 3551
F (65) 6749 3552
E customersvc@apdsing.com

Malaysia

APD Kuala Lumpur
Nos. 22, 24 & 26 Jalan SS3/41
47300 Petaling Jaya
Selangor Darul Ehsan
T (603) 7877 6063
F (603) 7877 3414
E liliankoe@apdkl.com

Indian Subcontinent

Roli Books
Kapil Kapoor
T +91 11 2921 0886
F +91 11 2921 7185
E kapilkapoor@rolibooks.com

Pakistan and Sri Lanka

Stephen Embrey
T+44 7952 919866
E s.embrey@thameshudson.co.uk

Australasia

Australia, New Zealand, Papua New Guinea & the Pacific Islands
Thames & Hudson Australia Pty Ltd
T (03) 9646 7788
E enquiries@thaust.com.au

For countries not mentioned, please contact:

Alexandra Levy
Export Sales
T +44 (0)20 7845 5038
E a.levy@thameshudson.co.uk

Steidl Berlin

Bildband Berlin UG
Immanuelkirchstraße 33
10405 Berlin
Germany
T +49 30 4737 7014

Steidl Göttingen

Buchhandlung Calvör
Jüdenstraße 23
37073 Göttingen
Germany
T +49 551 484800

Steidl East Hampton

Linde Gallery
25 A Newtown Lane
East Hampton, NY
11937 USA
T +1 6316045757

Steidl Hong Kong

Asia One
8 Fung Yip Street, Chai Wan
Hong Kong
China
T +852 2 8 892 320

Steidl Johannesburg

MAKER
At House Villa
75 4th Road
Kew
Johannesburg 2090
South Africa
T +27 11 447 6680
www.makerstudio.co.za

Steidl Lisbon

Stet
Rua Aćacio de Paira, 20A
1700-111 Lisboa
Portugal
T +35 1 936 250 198

Steidl Los Angeles

Rosegallery
Bergamot Station Arts Center
Gallery G5
2525 Michigan Avenue
Santa Monica, CA 90404
USA
T +1 3102648440

Steidl Ljubljana

Galerija Fotografija
gallery and bookshop
Levstikov trg 7
Ljubljana/Slovenia
T/F +38 612511529
M   +38 641664357
www.galerijafotografija.si

Steidl Madrid

La Fabrica
Verónica 13
28014 Madrid
Spain
T +34 912985537

Steidl Moscow

The Lumiere Brothers
Center of Photography
Red October, Bolotnaya emb., 3, b.1
119072 Moscow
Russia
T +7 4952289878
www.lumiere.ru

Steidl Paris

Librairie 7L
7, rue de Lille
75007 Paris
France
T +33 1 42920358

Steidl Rome

s.t. foto libreria galleria
Via Bartolomeo d'Alviano 2A
00176 Roma
Italy
T +39 338 4094647

Steidl San Diego

Museum of Photographic Arts
Museum Store
1649 El Prado
San Diego, CA 92101
USA
T +1 6192387559231

Steidl Tokyo

POST / limArt co., ltd
2-10-3-1F Ebisuminami
Shibuya-ku
150-0022 Tokyo
Japan
T +81 3 3713 8670
www.post-books.info

steidl.de

For detailed information on all our
books, artists and related events
please visit us at steidl.de

Nadav Kander

Mitch Epstein

Nan Goldin

Gordon Parks

Antanas Sutkus

Evelyn Hofer

Chris Killip

Mark Neville

Holger Sierks

Carsten Güttler

Cecilia Tubiana

Dayanita Singh

Massimo Vitali

Joel Sternfeld

John Gossage

Mat Hennek

Orhan Pamuk

Anastasia Samoylova

Juergen Teller

Francesco Bonami

Kanye West

Karl Lagerfeld

Justine Picardie

Samuel Fosso

Sebastian Posingis

RongRong

Charles H. Traub

Kai Wiedenhöfer

Donovan Wylie

Chris Klatell

Harf Zimmermann

Gleb Kosorukov

Christian Lesemann

Manfred Heiting

Hans Georg Näder

Tina Campt

Marianne Hirsch

Gil Hochberg

Brian Wallis

Caryl Englander

Henri Lustiger Thaler

New books

The cold, dark days and nights of fall and winter are traditionally a time to rest and contemplate. It's an occasion to hibernate, and not just for flora and fauna; booklovers too cherish their time indoors and turn to their bookshelves for solace, inspiration, and a good dash of color.

These thoughts have shaped our new Fall/Winter 2019/2020 program—printed books not just as curated vessels of text and image, but as companions.

As with all Steidl books, our new titles on the pages beyond will be made with the finest, most durable materials and all the know-how we can muster—to ensure they illuminate your bookshelves for many winters to come.

Benicio del Toro
from Nadav Kander's The Meeting

Donald Trump
from Nadav Kander's The Meeting

Desmond Tutu
from Nadav Kander's The Meeting

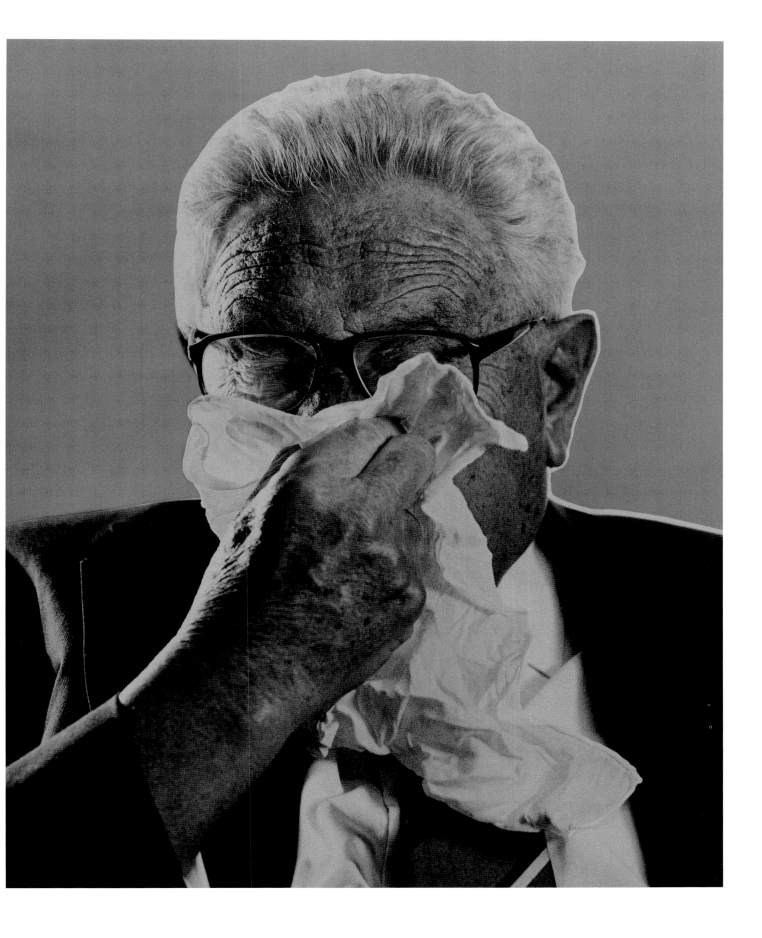

Henry Kissinger
from Nadav Kander's The Meeting

Michael Stipe

Christian Marclay

Ridley Scott

Robert Plant

Born in 1961, Nadav Kander lives and
works in London. Selected past projects
include "Yangtze - The Long River,"
winner of the Prix Pictet award in 2009;
"Dust," which explores the vestiges of
the Cold War through the radioactive
ruins of secret cities between Kazakhstan
and Russia; "Bodies 6 Women, 1 Man";
and "Obama's People," an acclaimed 52
portrait series commissioned by the New
York Times Magazine. Kander's work is
held in collections including the National
Portrait Gallery, London; the Museum
of Contemporary Photography, Chicago;
and the Statoil Collection, Norway. His
exhibitions include those at the Museum
of Photographic Arts, San Diego; the
Museum of Applied Arts, Cologne; and
Somerset House, London. Kander's recent
awards include an Honorary Fellowship
Award from the Royal Photographic Society
and the Sony Outstanding Contribution to
Photography Award 2019.

Regardless of his sitter—whether family member or influential
celebrity—Nadav Kander's portraiture shows what makes that particular individual *human*. His aim is to move beyond capturing an accurate
likeness—to access the emotions within, the uncertainty, the shadow
as much as the light, the complex sense of self that otherwise lays
hidden. "Revealed and concealed, beauty and destruction, ease and
disease, shame and shameless," explains Kander, "These paradoxes
are essential to all my work and represent what is common to all my
varied subject matter..." This collection, the first book dedicated his
portraiture, shows the range and nuance of Kander's work.

With his minimal and intuitive approach, Kander shows his
interest in universal experience, which transcends the specificity of
public persona or status. His enigmatic depictions of actors, artists,
musicians, authors, sports icons and political leaders—from Barack
Obama, John le Carré, Alexander McQueen, to Tracey Emin, Robert
Plant and Prince Charles—are layered and penetrating, revealing
unexpected moments of reverie and vulnerability.

*What I look to expose is what lies beneath the image, that which is
below the surface of what is seen.* Nadav Kander

Nadav Kander
The Meeting

Texts by David Lynch, Ian McEwan and Nadav Kander
Conversation between Nadav Kander and David Campany
Book design by Nadav Kander and Duncan Whyte /
Steidl Design
324 pages
10.6 × 13 in. / 27 × 33 cm
118 black-and-white and 151 color photographs
Tritone and four-color process
Clothbound hardcover

€ 85.00 / £ 80.00 / US$ 95.00
ISBN 978-3-95829-615-2

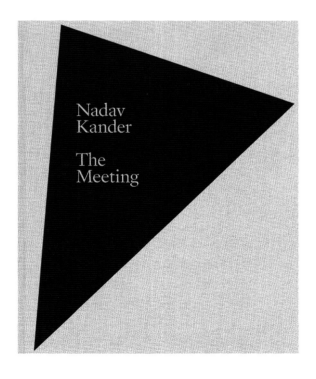

A pioneer of 1970s color photography, Mitch Epstein has photographed for half a century how we engage with our landscape. Epstein has won numerous awards including the Prix Pictet, the Berlin Prize and a Guggenheim Fellowship. His work is held in collections including the Museum of Modern Art and Tate Modern, and in 2013 the Walker Art Center commissioned a theatrical rendition of his "American Power" series. Epstein has conveyed the cultural and physical evolution of the United States from 1973 to the present in his Steidl books Family Business (2003), Recreation (2005), American Power (2011), New York Arbor (2013) and Rocks and Clouds (2017).

Mitch Epstein
Sunshine Hotel

Edited by Andrew Roth
Book design by Garrick Gott
264 pages
12.2 × 12 in. / 31 × 30.5 cm
13 black-and-white and 162 color photographs
Four-color process
Clothbound hardcover

€ 65.00 / £ 60.00 / US$ 75.00
ISBN 978-3-95829-609-1

America, as a place and an idea, has occupied Mitch Epstein's art for the past five decades. With the first photographs he made in 1969 at 16-years-old, Epstein began confronting the cultural psychology of the United States. Although he started working in an era defined by the Vietnam War, civil rights, rock and roll, and free love, he responded hardily to each radically different era that followed—from Reaganomics to surveillance after 9/11, to the current climate crisis and resurgence of white supremacy. More than a single era or issue, it is the living organism of American culture that engages Epstein; no matter how much the country changes, he describes something mysteriously and persistently American.

Conceived of and sequenced by Andrew Roth, *Sunshine Hotel* assembles 175 photos made between 1969 and 2018—more than half previously unpublished. Yet the book is not simply a retrospective. It traces both the evolution of an artist and the development of a country, revealing Epstein's formal and thematic shifts in tandem with America's changing zeitgeist and landscape. *Sunshine Hotel* is a visual immersion that forgoes linearity and a classical layout, as it sets forth Epstein's evolving understanding of his country's pathologies and promise.

Epstein raises the more challenging question of how inherently abstract political concepts about the nation and the culture as a whole can be represented photographically ... he addresses this crucial question head on, offering a new, non-didactic approach.
Brian Wallis

Co-published with PPP Editions

Exhibitions:
Sikkema Jenkins & Co., New York, 3 September to 5 October 2019
Galerie Thomas Zander, Cologne, fall 2019

Nan Goldin is one of the most eminent
photographers of our times, and today
lives and works between New York, Paris
and Berlin. Given her first camera at the
age of 15, she began taking Polaroids of
herself and those around her. In 1972 she
moved in with a group of drag queens in
Boston, starting her lifelong passion for
photographing her queer and transsexual
communities. In 1978 Goldin moved to New
York City, where she presented slideshows
in nightclubs and underground cinemas;
her best known, "The Ballad of Sexual
Dependency," was published as a landmark
book in 1986. In the nineties Goldin
relocated to Berlin where she published
A Double Life with David Armstrong and
the first edition of The Other Side. In
2000 she again moved to Paris, where
she was invited to create site-specific
works at the Louvre and now Versailles.
In 2018 Goldin and her colleagues
founded P.A.I.N. (Prescription Addiction
Intervention Now), a direct action group
fighting the pharmaceutical companies and
advocating for addiction treatment in
the mounting opioid crisis. The book has
been an important medium for Goldin over
the decades; her publications with Steidl
include The Beautiful Smile (2008) and
Diving for Pearls (2016).

This is an expanded and updated version of Nan Goldin's seminal
book *The Other Side*, originally published in 1993. There will be a
revised introduction by Goldin, and for the first time the voices of those
whose stories are represented. Now being released at a time when the
discourse around gender and sexual orientation is evolving, *The Other
Side* traces some of the history that informs this new visibility.

The first photographs in the book are from the 1970s, when Goldin
lived in Boston with a group of drag queens and documented their
glamour and vulnerability. In the early eighties, Goldin chronicled the
lives of transgender friends in New York when AIDS began to decimate
her community. In the nineties, she recorded the explosion of drag as
a social phenomenon in New York, Berlin and Bangkok, photographing
their public personas while showing their real lives backstage. Goldin's
newest photographs are intimate portraits, imbued with tenderness,
of some of her most beloved friends. *The Other Side* is her homage
to the queens she's loved, many of whom she's lost, over the last four
decades.

*The pictures in this book are not of people suffering gender dysphoria
but rather expressing gender euphoria...* Nan Goldin

Exhibition: Marian Goodman Gallery, London, October 2019

Nan Goldin
The Other Side

Texts by Nan Goldin and B.
Interview by Sunny Suits with Joey Gabriel
Book design by Nan Goldin, Holger Feroudj, Gerhard Steidl
192 pages
8.5 × 10.5 in. / 22 × 27 cm
20 black-and-white and 115 color photographs
Tritone and four-color process
Hardcover

€ 40.00 / £ 38.00 / US$ 45.00
ISBN 978-3-95829-613-8

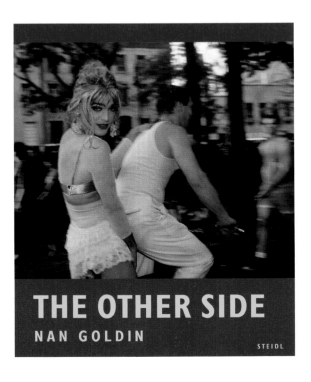

Gordon Parks was born into poverty and segregation in Fort Scott, Kansas, in 1912. An itinerant laborer, he worked as a brothel pianist and railcar porter, among other jobs, before buying a camera at a pawnshop, training himself, and becoming a photographer. In addition to his storied tenures photographing for the Farm Security Administration (1941-45) and Life magazine (1948-72), Parks evolved into a modern-day Renaissance man, finding success as a film director, writer and composer. The first African-American director to helm a major motion picture, he helped launch the blaxploitation genre with his film Shaft (1971). He wrote numerous memoirs, novels and books of poetry, and received many awards, including the National Medal of Arts and more than 50 honorary degrees. Parks died in 2006.

Gordon Parks
Muhammad Ali

Series editor: Peter W. Kunhardt, Jr.
Edited by Paul Roth and April Watson
Foreword by Peter W. Kunhardt Jr. and Julián Zugazagoitia
Introduction by Kareem Abdul-Jabbar
Texts by Gerald Early and April Watson
Book Design by Duncan Whyte / Steidl Design
176 pages
9.8 x 11.4 in. / 25 x 29 cm
110 black-and-white and 5 color photographs
Tritone and four-color process
Half-linen hardcover

€ 48.00 / £ 45.00 / US$ 55.00
ISBN 978-3-95829-619-0

In 1966 *Life* magazine assigned famed photographer Gordon Parks to cover Muhammad Ali, the brash young boxing champion. Four years later in 1970, the two came together again for a second feature story in "The Great American Magazine." These encounters framed a critical passage in the career of the controversial heavyweight, whose antiwar and black separatist views had led to widespread vilification in the United States. They also marked a significant moment of transition for Parks, then following up his remarkable success in photojournalism with new projects as an author, filmmaker and composer.

Collaborating on these two stories, Parks and Ali transcended their routine roles as journalist and athlete to make sense of an epoch and the American struggle against racial inequality, in which both were key players. Parks' intimate perspective on Ali during this crucial period is indispensable to understanding the boxer called "the greatest of all time." This book includes an expansive selection of photographs from Parks' original reportage, many never before published, as well as reproductions of his original stories as they appeared in *Life* magazine.

Both men were tenacious fighters. Both men bore the scars of lifelong racism. Both men were internationally acclaimed, yet both were more devoted to speaking out for social justice than seeking out personal success. Kareem Abdul-Jabbar, *Two Poets of Faith and Hope*

Co-published with The Gordon Parks Foundation and the Nelson-Atkins Museum of Art

Exhibition: Nelson-Atkins Museum of Art, Kansas City, 10 December 2019 to 6 July 2020

Born in Kluoniškiai, Lithuania, in
1939, Antanas Sutkus earned a degree
in journalism in Vilnius and worked for
daily newspapers before co-founding the
Lithuanian Photographers' Association in
1969, which he headed for many years.
Sutkus was president of the Union of
Lithuanian Art Photographers upon its
establishment in 1996 and has been its
honorary president since 2009. He is
the recipient of the Lithuanian National
Culture and Arts Award and the Order of
the Lithuanian Grand Duke Gedimas, an
Erna and Victor Hasselblad Foundation
Grant and the 2017 Erich Salomon Award
of the Deutsche Gesellschaft für
Photographie. Sutkus has exhibited
extensively, including his 2018
retrospective at the National Gallery
of Art in Vilnius on the hundredth
anniversary of the Republic of Lithuania,
for which Steidl published planet
lithuania.

Antanas Sutkus
Pro Memoria

Edited by Thomas Schirmböck
Book design by Steidl Design
128 pages
9.3 × 10.4 in. / 23.5 × 26.5 cm
87 black-and-white photographs
Tritone
Clothbound hardcover

€ 35.00 / £ 30.00 / US$ 40.00
ISBN 978-3-95829-640-4

Born in 1939, Antanas Sutkus learnt of the mass killing of the Jews already during World War II from his grandparents. He felt bitterly opposed to the humiliation and human destruction that occurred in his homeland Lithuania, experiencing shame and guilt for the atrocities committed behind the Vilijampole ghetto gates and the Ninth Fort. During the "Sonderaktion 1005" between 1942 and '44, German occupation forces tried to vanish the relics of the victims. In 1988 Sutkus began photographing the Kaunas Jews who had escaped death in concentration camps; *Pro Memoria* presents a selection of these portraits, and evidences the relationships Sutkus forged with his sitters.

As far back as the time of Grand Duke Gediminas (1275–1341), who invited tradesmen and artisans to Lithuania from various European states, the Jews had been offered protection and support there. Over the next 600 years they took root in Lithuania through their accomplishments and prayers, printing workshops and synagogues, libraries and gymnasiums, song and legends. This vibrant branch of Lithuania's cultural history was then violently destroyed when 200,000 Jews were murdered and thrown into pits on forest edges, quarries and death camps. This book is a tribute to these people, and an expression of attempts at understanding, penitence, purification and rebirth.

If photography can make any claim to universal experience it is through being particular. Sutkus' photographs are as rich in particulars as any in the history of the medium. Rarely are they overtly political, but inevitably the complex historical passage of his country has left its impression upon the fate and hopes, and thus the bodies and faces of those who have come before his camera. David Campany

Born in 1922 in Marburg, Evelyn Hofer
grew up in Switzerland and Spain. She
completed photographic apprenticeships
in Basel and Zurich before studying under
Hans Finsler, and in 1946 settled in New
York. Hofer's career took a decisive
turn with her photos for Mary McCarthy's
The Stones of Florence (1959); books on
London, Spain, New York, Washington and
Dublin followed, as well as Emerson in
Italy (1989). In the 1970s Hofer focused
on society-related subjects and published
photo-essays in Life and the New York
Times Magazine. She also photographed
public figures, interiors for magazines,
and in later life primarily personal
subjects. Hofer died in Mexico City in
2009.

The starting point for this book is Evelyn Hofer's *Dublin: A Portrait*, which features an in-depth essay by V. S. Pritchett and photos by Hofer, and enjoyed great popularity upon its original publication in 1967. *Dublin: A Portrait* is an example of Hofer's perhaps most important body of work, her city portraits: books that present comprehensive prose texts by renowned authors alongside her self-contained visual essays with their own narratives. *Dublin: A Portrait* was the last book published in this renowned series.

The newly conceived *Dublin* focuses on the photos Hofer took on behalf of the publisher Harper & Row in 1965 and 1966. In Dublin Hofer repeatedly turned her camera to sights of the city, but mainly to the people who constituted its essence. She made numerous portraits— be they of writers and public figures or unknown people in the streets. Her portraits give evidence of an intense, respectful engagement with her subjects, who participate as equal partners in the process of photographing.

While working on my Dublin book, I found many people shy and reluctant to be photographed. Therefore, I tried to meet the person first, just to talk, to show my respect... Evelyn Hofer

Evelyn Hofer
Dublin

Edited by Andreas Pauly and Sabine Schmid
Book design by Steidl Design
160 pages
8.7 × 11.2 in. / 22 × 28.5 cm
63 black-and-white and 14 color photographs
Tritone and four-color process
Clothbound hardcover with a tipped-in photograph

€ 45.00 / £ 40.00 / US$ 50.00
ISBN 978-3-95829-632-9

Born on the Isle of Man in 1946,
Chris Killip was a Professor of Visual
and Environmental Studies at Harvard
University where he had taught from 1991.
Since 2012 he has held solo exhibitions
at Museum Folkwang, Essen; Le Bal, Paris;
Tate Britain, London; Museo Reina Sofia,
Madrid; and the J. Paul Getty Museum, Los
Angeles. Killip's works are held in the
permanent collections of institutions
including the Museum of Modern Art, New
York; George Eastman House, Rochester;
and the Victoria and Albert Museum,
London. His books with Steidl are Pirelli
Work (2006), Seacoal, (2011), Arbeit /
Work (2012), Isle of Man Revisited (2015)
and In Flagrante Two (2016).

Late in 2016 Chris Killip's son serendipitously discovered a box of
contact sheets of the photos his father had made at The Station,
an anarcho-punk music venue in Gateshead open from 1981 to 1985.
These images of raw youth caught in the heat of celebration had
lain dormant for 30 years; they now return to life in this book. The
Station was not merely a music and rehearsal space, but a crucible
for the self-expression of the sub-cultures and punk politics of the
time. As Killip recollects: "When I first went to The Station in April
1985, I was amazed by the energy and feel of the place. It was totally
different, run for and by the people who went there. Every Saturday
that I could, I photographed there. Nobody ever asked me where I
was from or even who I was. A 39-year-old with cropped white hair,
always wearing a suit, with pockets stitched inside the jacket to hold
my slides. With a 4 × 5 camera around my neck and a Norman flash and
its battery around my waist, I must have looked like something out of
a 1950s B movie. 1985 was just after the miners strike and there was
a lot of youth unemployment. Most of the punks at The Station didn't
have a job, and this place, run as a very inclusive collective, was so
important to them and their self-worth."

*What you're trying not to do is oversimplify. You're trying to have some
sort of cool in there somehow, so that people looking at your pictures
are not constrained by you. Meaning you haven't predetermined
everything, so that ambiguity can be embraced.* Chris Killip

Chris Killip
The Station

Text by Chris Killip
Book design by Pony Ltd.
80 pages
11.4 × 15 in. / 29 × 38 cm
72 black-and-white photographs
Tritone
Hardcover

€ 75.00 / £ 70.00 / US$ 85.00
ISBN 978-3-95829-616-9

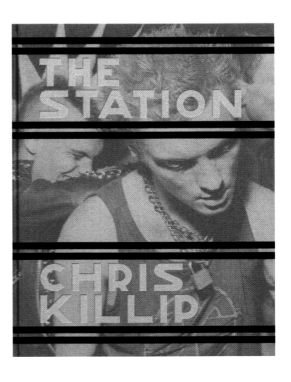

Mark Neville, born in London in 1966,
studied at Goldsmiths, London, and the
Rijksakademie, Amsterdam. In 2013 his
project "Deeds Not Words" was shown at
The Photographers' Gallery London, and
in 2017 his Pulitzer Prize nominated
series "Here Is London" was exhibited
at the Multimedia Art Museum of Moscow.
Neville's exhibitions include those at
Haus der Kunst, Munich; Jeu de Paume,
Paris; and Tate Britain. His monograph
Fancy Pictures, published by Steidl, was
nominated for Book of the Year at the
2017 Paris Photo-Aperture Foundation
Photobook Awards.

Since 2015 Mark Neville has been documenting life in Ukraine, with subjects ranging from holidaymakers on the beaches of Odessa, to the Roma communities on the Hungarian border, the churchgoers and nightclubbers, to those internally displaced by the war in Eastern Ukraine.

Employing his activist strategy of a targeted book dissemination, Neville is committed to making a direct impact upon the war in Ukraine. He will distribute 2,000 copies free to policy makers, opinion makers, members of parliament both in Ukraine and Russia, members of the international community and its media, as well as those involved directly in the Minsk Agreements. He means to re-ignite awareness and concern about the war, galvanize the peace talks, and attempt to halt the daily bombing and casualties in Eastern Ukraine which have been occurring for five years now. Neville's images will be accompanied by writings from both Russian and Ukrainian novelists, as well as texts from policy makers and the international community, to suggest how to end the current intransigence and protracted conflict.

Mark Neville has re-imagined what documentary photography could be, should be. Instead of the bland "deconstructions" that pass so lazily as "critical" in contemporary art, he makes extraordinary pictures and finds extraordinary ways to get them back to those he has photographed. David Campany

Mark Neville
Ukraine – Stop Tanks with Books

Edited by David Campany
Book design by Steidl Design
192 pages
11.8 × 10.6 in. / 30 × 27 cm
20 black-and-white and 60 color photographs
Tritone and four-color process
Clothbound hardcover with a tipped-in photograph

€ 48.00 / £ 45.00 / US$ 60.00
ISBN 978-3-95829-618-3

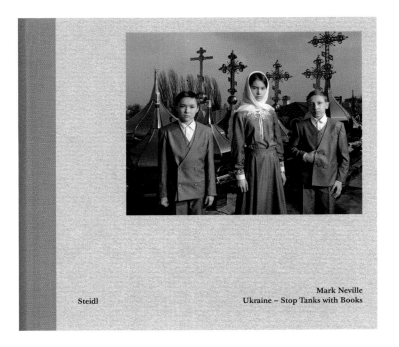

Steidl

Mark Neville
Ukraine – Stop Tanks with Books

I will always be a musician. A musician will always be a musician, not just me. He may stop performing but the musician is still there.

I may be just teaching, bringing up a lot of students, that's something I would like to do. Have a nice little place in the country some where, sit back, teach, bring up kids and try to make them aware of my culture, whatever that may be at that time.

I enjoy my work so much, that whatever discrepancies arise, go unnoticed or they do not have a lasting effect on me. The only lasting effect on our physical being, our mental, our person, is music. So whenever music happens, which is most of the time, it has this effect of making everything better whether I am upset, sad or just tired. Maybe its a dream world, maybe its make believe, but its beautiful.

Top left:
Zakir and his nephew Ehtesham
Bottom left:
Zakir's 6 yr old daughter Ameena
Qureshi.

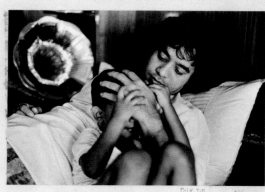

ZAKIR HUSSAIN

In a musicians house there is no fixed time that you start learning. Its there all around you, continuously seeping into your ears. I was completely fascinated by the sounds these funny rounded objects produced.

There was no formal training. I used to pick up the tablas and bang on them whenever I could and get tips from people who came to learn from my father. It was not until I started playing school concerts, that my father decided to teach me. It is difficult to be the son of this great tabla player. As this great man's son good is expected of you. You have to be better than good or now will find that you just live in the shadows of this great master.

Dayanita Singh was born in New Delhi
in 1961 and studied at the National
Institute of Design in Ahmedabad and the
International Center of Photography in
New York. Singh's exhibitions include
those at the Serpentine Gallery in London,
Hamburger Bahnhof in Berlin, the Hayward
Gallery in London, the Art Institute of
Chicago, and the Museum für Moderne Kunst
in Frankfurt. In 2013 Singh represented
Germany at the Venice Biennale. Bookmaking
is central to her practice. Singh's books
with Steidl include Privacy (2004), Go
Away Closer (2007), Sent a Letter (2007),
Dream Villa (2010), File Room (2013),
Museum of Chance (2014) and Museum Bhavan,
Book of the Year at the 2017 Paris Photo-
Aperture Foundation Photobook Awards and
recipient of the 2018 ICP Infinity Award
for Artist's Book.

The book is well known as Dayanita Singh's primary medium, one she explores to create new relationships between photography, publishing, the exhibition and the museum. But where did her passion for the book as the ideal vessel for her photos, for the stories she tells, begin? The answer lies in *Zakir Hussain*, a handmade maquette Singh crafted in 1986 as her first project as a graphic design student. The protagonist of Singh's photo essay is the Indian classical tabla virtuoso Zakir Hussain, whom she captured on the stage and at home with his family. Surrounding the photos are handwritten texts gleaned from interviews Singh made with her sitters, including insights from Hussain: "I will always be a musician. A musician will always be a musician, not just me. He may stop performing but the musician is still there."

This Steidl facsimile edition is scanned from Singh's original maquette and reproduces all its "imperfections" and idiosyncrasies including her pencilled notes about the book's construction—indications of the influential bookmaker to come. Shanay Jhaveri's accompanying essay discusses how Singh came to "make" the original, referring to her student notes and exploring how she intuitively assembled the book, from editing the images to design, setting the ground for the book objects and photo architectures of her later practice.

Making the book is my work. The photographs are just the raw material. I make photographs to make books, and I now make books to make book objects. Dayanita Singh

Dayanita Singh
Zakir Hussain Maquette

Text by Shanay Jhaveri
Conversation between Dayanita Singh,
Gerhard Steidl and Monte Packham
Book design by Dayanita Singh
8.5 × 9.1 in. / 21.7 × 23.2 cm

Maquette
96 pages
94 black-and-white photographs

Reader
32 pages
15 black-and-white images

Poster
26 × 29 in. / 66 × 73.6 cm
14 black-and-white images

Four-color process
Two softcovers and a poster in a sleeve

€ 40.00 / £ 35.00 / US$ 45.00
ISBN 978-3-95829-623-7

Poster

Maquette

Reader

Sleeve

BAWA
CHAIRS

Dayanita Singh was born in New Delhi in 1961 and studied at the National Institute of Design in Ahmedabad and the International Center of Photography in New York. Singh's exhibitions include those at the Serpentine Gallery in London, Hamburger Bahnhof in Berlin, the Hayward Gallery in London, the Art Institute of Chicago, and the Museum für Moderne Kunst in Frankfurt. In 2013 Singh represented Germany at the Venice Biennale. Bookmaking is central to her practice. Singh's books with Steidl include Privacy (2004), Go Away Closer (2007), Sent a Letter (2007), Dream Villa (2010), File Room (2013), Museum of Chance (2014) and Museum Bhavan, Book of the Year at the 2017 Paris Photo-Aperture Foundation Photobook Awards and recipient of the 2018 ICP Infinity Award for Artist's Book.

"I wanted to suggest a conversation among these chairs, which have always seemed to me more like people than objects, with distinct personalities and genders even." With this sentiment in mind, Dayanita Singh went about photographing the many chairs living throughout the houses and public buildings designed by Geoffrey Bawa (1919–2003), whom Singh deems a "tropical modernist" and the most influential architect of the South Asian region. Less still lifes than portraits, Singh's images show how Bawa's spaces engage with the chairs, be they designed or collected by Bawa, or installed after his passing. Made to celebrate the hundredth anniversary of Bawa's birth, *Bawa Chairs* is constructed as an accordion-fold booklet in the manner of Singh's *Chairs* (2005), *Sent a Letter* (2007) and *Museum Bhavan* (2017), and intended to be unfolded and installed at will—transforming the book into an exhibition, and the reader into a curator.

I want something ordinary on the outside and like a jewel inside.
Dayanita Singh

Exhibitions:
Frith Street Gallery, London, October 2019
Callicoon Fine Arts, New York, October 2019
Barefoot Gallery, Colombo, December 2019

Dayanita Singh
Bawa Chairs

Book design by Dayanita Singh
27 pages
3.5 × 5.4 in. / 9 × 13.7 cm
27 black-and-white photographs
Tritone
Accordion-fold booklet

€ 20.00 / £ 18.00 / US$ 25.00
ISBN 978-3-95829-673-2

Born in Como in 1944, Massimo Vitali studied photography at the London College of Printing. Beginning in the sixties Vitali worked as a photojournalist, collaborating with magazines and agencies throughout Europe, before turning to cinematography for television and cinema in the early eighties. He eventually returned to still photography as an artist, taking up large-format photography in 1993 and beginning his famous "Beach Series" in 1995. Steidl has published Vitali's Landscape with Figures (2004) and Landscape with Figures / Natural Habitats, 1994-2009 (2011).

After nearly 30 years working with large-format photography, Massimo Vitali brings together his twelve "best" photographs in this volume. The selection of just a handful of works was made following many lengthy conversations with collaborators and curators who know Vitali's photography deeply. The chosen works are not necessarily his most well-known pieces; rather each speaks to a particular moment of his artistic research. The different images unfold in a changing world that is reflected in the landscapes depicted and the human interactions with them. Twelve photographs like twelve months in a year: short stories in a long career.

My photography comes from absolute matter-of-fact situations but also from a deep curiosity that I possess for people, for what they do and how they think. Massimo Vitali

Massimo Vitali
Short Stories

Book design by Holger Feroudj and Paloma Tarrio Alves / Steidl Design
48 pages
12.6 × 12.8 in. / 32 × 32,5 cm
12 color photographs tipped-in by hand
Four-color process
Clothbound hardcover in a slipcase

€ 125.00 / £ 120.00 / US$ 145.00
ISBN 978-3-95829-496-7

Slipcase

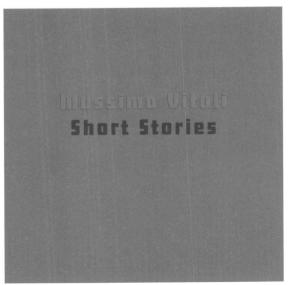

Book

Born in Como in 1944, Massimo Vitali studied photography at the London College of Printing. Beginning in the sixties Vitali worked as a photojournalist, collaborating with magazines and agencies throughout Europe, before turning to cinematography for television and cinema in the early eighties. He eventually returned to still photography as an artist, taking up large-format photography in 1993 and beginning his famous "Beach Series" in 1995. Steidl has published Vitali's Landscape with Figures (2004) and Landscape with Figures / Natural Habitats, 1994–2009 (2011).

Steidl is committed to publishing the ongoing life's work of Massimo Vitali, and *Entering a New World*, collecting images from 2009 to 2018, is the newest book in this series. Following the first two now out-of-print volumes published together as *Landscape with Figures / Natural Habitats, 1994–2009* in 2011, this book presents Vitali's large-scale color images of humans interacting en masse—both consciously and unconsciously—with their environments. Whether relaxing beachside, exploring the ruins of the Roman Forum or navigating a crowded shopping promenade, Vitali's pictures are topographical celebrations and subtle critiques of our changing habits of leisure. *Entering a New World* furthermore traces an important shift in Vitali's practice: his move from large-format film to medium-format digital.

Photography is like a river with a thousand streams that never converge. Massimo Vitali

Massimo Vitali
Entering a New World
Photographs 2009–2018

Book design by Massimo Vitali and Steidl Design
208 pages
14.2 × 11.4 in. / 36 × 29 cm
115 color photographs
Four-color process
Clothbound hardcover with dust jacket

€ 95.00 / £ 90.00 / US$ 125.00
ISBN 978-3-95829-626-8

A major figure in the photography world, Joel Sternfeld was born in New York City in 1944. He has received numerous awards including two Guggenheim fellowships, a Prix de Rome and the Citibank Photography Award. Sternfeld's books published by Steidl include American Prospects (2003), Sweet Earth (2006), Oxbow Archive (2008), First Pictures (2012), and Landscape as Longing (2016) with Frank Gohlke.

In the early morning of 14 April 2018, David Buckel walked into Prospect Park in New York City and set himself alight. He was a distinguished attorney whose work to secure social justice and LGBT rights had won national acclaim. At the time of his death at the age of 60 Buckel had left the practice of law and was working on a community farm in Red Hook, Brooklyn, as the head of composting. He was married to a man with whom he, and a married lesbian couple, were co-raising a college-bound daughter.

In an email sent to the *New York Times* moments before his death Buckel decried the increasing pollution of the earth. He expressed the hope that his death by fossil fuels would encourage others to be better stewards and cohabitants of the earth. Joel Sternfeld happened to be in Prospect Park on that day with his nine-year-old son. Returning the next day he began to document the gradual regeneration of the site as a means to honor the hope that climate change might be reversed. *Our Loss* is the latest book by Sternfeld in his ongoing exploration of the effects of climate change, following *Oxbow Archive* (2008) and *When it Changed* (2008).

The seasons are the blatant manifestation of the physical forces of the universe: energy from the sun, gravity, material from the origin— and of all the biologic particulars of this planet; oxygen, water, life forms, all showing up, and showing off together. Joel Sternfeld

Joel Sternfeld
Our Loss

Book design by Joel Sternfeld and Holger Feroudj /Steidl Design
144 pages
12 × 9.3 in. / 30.5 × 28 cm
60 color photographs
Four-color process
Clothbound hardcover with a tipped-in photograph

€ 58.00 / £ 55.00 / US$ 60.00
ISBN 978-3-95829-658-9

OUR LOSS
JOEL STERNFELD

Steidl

A major figure in the photography world,
Joel Sternfeld was born in New York City
in 1944. He has received numerous awards
including two Guggenheim fellowships, a
Prix de Rome and the Citibank Photography
Award. Sternfeld's books published by
Steidl include American Prospects (2003),
Sweet Earth (2006), Oxbow Archive (2008),
First Pictures (2012), and Landscape as
Longing (2016) with Frank Gohlke.

Joel Sternfeld
Rome after Rome

Text by Joel Sternfeld
Book design by Joel Sternfeld and
Victor Balko / Steidl Design
112 pages
18.9 × 15.7 in. / 48 × 40 cm
74 color photographs
Four-color process
Clothbound hardcover with a tipped-in photo

€ 145.00 / £ 135.00 / US$ 175.00
ISBN 978-3-95829-263-5

In his 1992 book *Campagna Romana. The Countryside of Ancient Rome* Joel Sternfeld focused on the ruins of grand structures with a clear warning: great civilizations fall, ours may too. Now in *Rome after Rome*, containing images from the previous book as well as numerous unpublished pictures, Sternfeld's questions multiply: who are these modern Romans? What is their relationship to the splendor that was? What is the nature of sullied modernity in relation to the Arcadian ideal? Is there, at this late moment, any chance for Utopia?

The Campagna, the countryside south and east of Rome occupies a special place in Roman—and human history. With the rise of Ancient Rome, this once polluted, malarial landscape was restored by emperors and thrived with some 20 towns and numerous wealthy villas on the rolling plains among the mighty aqueducts that fed water to Rome. After the city fell, the Campagna once again became desolate and dangerous. The gloomy tombs, broken homes and aqueducts sat in a kind of no man's land for over 1,000 years.

To this landscape came the painters: Dürer, Lorrain, Poussin, and later, Corot, Turner, and Americans such as Thomas Cole. In the ruins they sought the origins of Rome's greatness and the meaning of her fall. Later they depicted a place where Roman gods cavorted and mankind lived in a golden age, an Arcadia. Central Rome was rebuilt with Baroque apartments hiding the past: in the Campagna the past was visible and all imaginings possible.

Sternfeld juxtaposes the ruins of a powerful, ancient civilization with the new construction and the debris of our own time. Avoiding obvious contrasts, eschewing heavy-handed irony, this contemporary artist draws our attention to both despoliation and lasting beauty; he suggests many reasons for despair, yet he also has something to say about the nobility of the human spirit. Theodore E. Stebbins Jr.

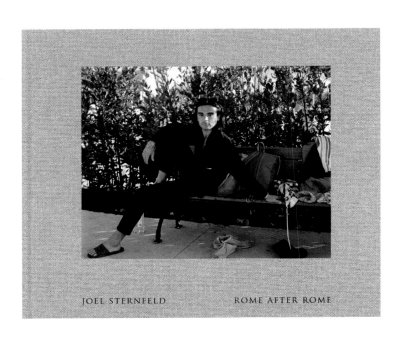

A major figure in the photography world,
Joel Sternfeld was born in New York City
in 1944. He has received numerous awards
including two Guggenheim fellowships, a
Prix de Rome and the Citibank Photography
Award. Sternfeld's books published by
Steidl include American Prospects (2003),
Sweet Earth (2006), Oxbow Archive (2008),
First Pictures (2012), and Landscape as
Longing (2016) with Frank Gohlke.

First published in 1987 to critical acclaim, the seminal American
Prospects has been likened to Walker Evans' *American Photographs*
and Robert Frank's *The Americans* in both its ability to visually
summarize the zeitgeist of a decade and to influence the course
of photography following its publication. This definitive edition of
American Prospects contains twelve new pictures, most of which
have neither been published nor exhibited. Freed from the size con-
straints of previous editions, Sternfeld includes portraits and portraits
in the landscape which elucidate the human condition in America. The
result is a more complex and rounded view of American society that
strongly anticipates Sternfeld's "Stranger Passing" series (1985–2000)
and links the two bodies of work.

*If the contamination of paradise has often been Sternfeld's subject,
he has likewise tainted the purity of photography in order to capture
the condition of America. His shift from spontaneous snapshot to
predetermined picture-making helped open the gates for a new type
of photography now practiced by Gregory Crewdson, Rineke Dijkstra,
Andreas Gursky, Thomas Ruff, Thomas Struth and Jeff Wall, among
many others.* Kerry Brougher, former chief curator of the Hirshhorn
Museum and Sculpture Garden

Joel Sternfeld
American Prospects - Revised Edition

Essays by Kerry Brougher, Andy Grundberg
and Anne W. Tucker
Book design by Joel Sternfeld and Gerhard Steidl
168 pages
15.4 x 12 in. / 39 x 30.5 cm
74 photographs
Four-colour process
Clothbound hardcover with dust jacket

€ 98.00 / £ 90.00 / $ 125.00
ISBN 978-3-95829-669-5

John Gossage, born in New York in 1946 and
now residing in Washington, D.C., studied
with Lisette Model and Alexey Brodovitch
in 1960-61. In the late 1960s he learned
Telecaster guitar from Roy Buchanan and
Danny Gatton, leaving professional music
in 1973 to return to photography. Between
1974 and 1990 Gossage exhibited at Leo
Castelli Gallery in New York; since 1990
he has concentrated almost exclusively on
publications, producing over 20 titles.
His books with Steidl include The Thirty-
Two Inch Ruler (2010), Looking up Ben
James - A Fable (2018) and Should Nature
Change (2019).

In John Gossage's words this is a book "with a particular context, of
photographs to settle the feeling that I did not understand about my
home. To do that I set out, starting in 2003, to see what clarity my
pictures might bring." And so came into being these photos of scenes,
things, minor events and the look in the eyes of the young, all taken
in everyday non-iconic places throughout his travels across America.
Gossage's ongoing look at his country within these pages is like a
dance: rhythmic, redeeming, restorative, intuitive; but tentatively
hopeful. "I would like to believe all of it," he writes, "that we will be
saved, but on Connecticut Avenue there is graffiti that says 'Where
is Lee Harvey Oswald when we need him?' All I can hear is the faint
echoing gun shots coming from Wounded Knee." To be continued...

The one thing that can solve most of our problems is dancing.
James Brown

John Gossage
Jack Wilson's Waltz

Text by John Gossage
Book design by John Gossage
144 pages
9.4 x 11.4 in. / 24 x 29 cm
69 black-and-white photographs
Quadratone
Clothbound hardcover with dust jacket

€ 45.00 / £ 40.00 / US$ 50.00
ISBN 978-3-95829-547-6

Mat Hennek was born in the Black Forest
area of Germany in 1969 and today lives
with his partner, the French pianist
Hélène Grimaud, in upstate New York
and California. While previously based
in Berlin, Hennek created influential
photographic portraits for the
entertainment and music industries,
before turning his attention to natural
landscapes. He has held solo exhibitions
throughout Europe, Asia and the USA.
Steidl published Hennek's Woodlands
project in 2017, which he presented
with Grimaud as the multimedia concert
Woodlands and Beyond... at Hamburg's
Elbphilharmonie, combining his photos
with her performance of romantic and
impressionistic compositions.

Silent Cities presents Mat Hennek's portraits of some of the world's
great cities—from New York, Los Angeles and London, to Tokyo,
Munich and Abu Dhabi—yet all curiously lacking people. Conceived
and constructed by man as vessels for human activity, these metrop-
olises are transformed by Hennek into monuments of silence: empty,
sometimes eerie sites for rituals of work and recreation that are yet
to take place. Whether the shimmering windows of a Dallas office
building, a lush Hong Kong garden of palms, blooms and fountains, the
famed pastel terraced facades of Monaco, or rows of trolleys outside
the concrete bulk of Paris' Charles de Gaulle airport, Hennek's
pictures demonstrate a consistent formal rigor and recast familiar
environments as new sources for focus and reflection.

*His photographs [...] collect so many elements that they have the
power of mandalas, representing the universe in a fragment, and
provoking a state of pure contemplation: in the simple experience of
gazing, everything becomes pure.* Laureline Amanieux

Mat Hennek
Silent Cities

Book design by Mat Hennek and Gerhard Steidl
120 pages
9.5 × 12.6 in. / 24 x 32 cm
80 color photographs
Four-color process
Clothbound hardcover

€ 45.00 / £ 40.00 / US$ 50.00
ISBN 978-3-95829-655-8

Orhan Pamuk is a writer-artist who won
the Nobel Prize for Literature in 2006.
Born in Istanbul in 1952, Pamuk intended
until the age of 22 to be a painter and
was thus encouraged by his family. In the
1960s and '70s, as he describes in his
book of autobiographical essays Istanbul
(2003), he photographed the streets of
Istanbul to use in his paintings; his
early desire to take photos is explored
in the introduction to the illustrated
version of Istanbul (2017). The Museum
of Innocence is both a novel Pamuk
published in 2008 and a museum he opened
in Istanbul in 2012 that exhibits the
objects, pictures, papers and photographs
described in the story. The Museum of
Innocence received the European Museum
of the Year Award in 2014. Pamuk has now
been taking photos for over 50 years;
Steidl published his first photobook
Balkon in 2018.

The dominant color in Orhan Pamuk's new book of photographs is
orange. When the Nobel-Prize-winning novelist is finished with a day's
writing, he takes his camera and wanders through Istanbul's various
neighborhoods. He often explores the backstreets of his hometown,
areas without tourists, spaces that seem neglected and forgotten,
washed in a particular light. This is the orange light of the windows and
streetlamps that Pamuk knows so well from his childhood in Istanbul
50 years ago, as he tells in his introduction. Yet Pamuk also observes
how the homely, cozy orange light is slowly being replaced by a new,
bright and icy-white light from the more modernized light bulbs. His
continuous walks in the backstreets is about recording and preserving
the comforting effect of the old, disappearing orange light, as well as
recognizing this new white vision. Whether reflected in well-trodden
snow, concentrated as a glaring ball atop a lamppost, or subtly
present as a diffuse haze, orange literally and aesthetically gives shape
to Pamuk's pictures, which reveal to us unseen corners of his home
city and inside this creative artist's mind.

There is genius in Pamuk's madness. Umberto Eco

Orhan Pamuk
Orange

Text by Orhan Pamuk
Book design by Orhan Pamuk, Holger Feroudj
and Gerhard Steidl
184 pages
6.9 × 9.8 in. / 17.6 × 25 cm
350 color photographs
Four-color process
Clothbound hardcover with a tipped-in photograph
and bookmark

€ 38.00 / £ 35.00 / US$ 45.00
ISBN 978-3-95829-653-4

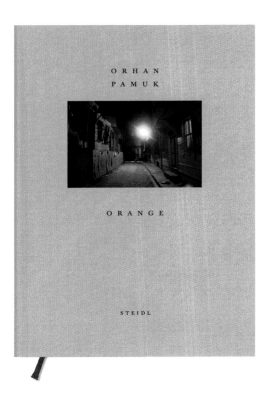

Born in Moscow in 1984, Anastasia
Samoylova moves between observational
photography, studio practice and
installation. She has exhibited at the
Aperture Foundation, New York; the
Griffin Museum of Photography, Boston;
and at festivals in Brazil, Belgium,
France, Holland, China, South Korea and
Germany. Samoylova has published her work
in Smithsonian Magazine, FOAM, Art Press,
Monocle and Bloomberg Businessweek.

FloodZone is Anastasia Samoylova's photographic account of life on the climatic knife-edge of the southern United States. Serious climate change is upon us, but this is not a visualization of disaster or catastrophe. These beautifully subtle and often unsettling images capture the mood of waiting, of knowing the climate is changing, of living with it. The color palette is tropical: lush greens, azure blues, pastel pinks. But the mood is pensive and melancholy.

As new luxury high-rises soar, their foundations are in water. Crumbling walls carry images of tourist paradise. In the heat and humidity nature threatens to return the place to tangled wilderness. Manatees appear in odd places, sensitive to environmental change. Liquid permeates Samoylova's urban scenes and unexpected views: waves, ripples, puddles, pools, splashes and spray. Water is every-where and water is the problem. Mixing lyric documentary, gently staged photos and epic aerial vistas, *FloodZone* crosses boundaries to express the deep contradictions of the place. The carefully paced sequence of photographs, arranged as interlocking chapters, make no judgment. They simply show; elegant, sincere, acute and perhaps redemptive.

The coast of the southern United States looks and feels like a paradise, but all is not what it seems. As sea levels rise and hurricanes threaten, the beauty of the place becomes bittersweet. The future is uncertain but life goes on. FloodZone *is a book about living with the contradiction.* Anastasia Samoylova

Exhibition: USF Contemporary Art Museum, Tampa, 2020

Anastasia Samoylova
FloodZone

Text by David Campany
Book design by Steidl Design
136 pages
9.1 x 10.8 × in. / 23.1 x 27.4 cm
17 black-and-white and 69 color photographs
Four-color process
Clothbound hardcover with dust jacket

€ 45.00 / £ 40.00 / US$ 50.00
ISBN 978-3-95829-633-6

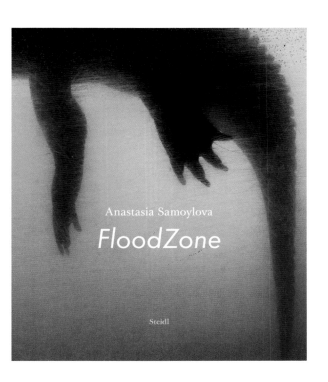

Juergen Teller, born in Erlangen, Germany, in 1964, studied at the Bayerische Staatslehranstalt für Photographie in Munich. His work has been published in influential magazines such as Vogue, System, i-D, POP and Arena Homme+, and has been the subject of solo exhibitions including those at the Institute of Contemporary Arts in London, the Fondation Cartier pour l'art contemporain in Paris and Martin-Gropius-Bau in Berlin. Teller won the prestigious Citibank Photography Prize in 2003, and from 2014 to 2019 held a professorship at the Akademie der Bildenden Künste Nürnberg. His books with Steidl include Louis XV (2005), Marc Jacobs Advertising, 1998-2009 (2009), Siegerflieger (2015) and The Master IV (2019).

"In 1999 I did a book called *Go-Sees* where girls came knocking on my door over a one-year period to show their portfolio and themselves. Recently, walking through Paris, I found myself thinking what work I would exhibit in my upcoming museum show in Naples. *Handbags, I'm just gonna do a handbag book and a show*. It felt like another *Go-Sees* book to me. Friends of my girlfriend were asking me what kind of a photographer I am, what I photograph. I replied: 'Actually, come to think of it, mostly handbags.' I always like their astonished and disappointed faces! I realized through the 30 years of my career, I photographed a hell of a lot of handbags within my fashion work. And as the Americans once said to me, 'Where's the money shot?' I looked at them puzzled. 'Show me the money shot!' they repeated. Here they are: the money shots in this collection of images for my new book." *Juergen Teller*

Juergen Teller
Handbags

Book design by Juergen Teller
608 pages
9.5 × 11.9 in. / 24 × 30.2 cm
600 color photographs
Four-color process
Clothbound hardcover with dust jacket and bookmark

€ 95.00 / £ 85.00 / US$ 125.00
ISBN 978-3-95829-634-3

JUERGEN TELLER HANDBAGS

Steidl

Born in Florence in 1955, Francesco Bonami is a renowned art critic and curator. He studied at the Accademia di Belle Arti Firenze and in the early nineties moved to the US where he was senior curator at the Museum of Contemporary Art in Chicago. In 2002 Bonami was artistic director of Turin's Fondazione Sandretto Re Rebaudengo, and in 2003 he was director of the fiftieth Venice Biennale. His books include Si crede Picasso. Come distinguere un vero artista contemporaneo da uno che non lo è (2010) and L'arte nel cesso. Da Duchamp a Cattelan, ascesa e declino dell'arte contemporanea (2017).

Juergen Teller, born in Erlangen, Germany, in 1964, studied at the Bayerische Staatslehranstalt für Photographie in Munich. His work has been published in influential magazines such as Vogue, System, i-D, POP and Arena Homme+, and has been the subject of solo exhibitions including those at the Institute of Contemporary Arts in London, the Fondation Cartier pour l'art contemporain in Paris and Martin-Gropius-Bau in Berlin. Teller won the prestigious Citibank Photography Prize in 2003, and from 2014 to 2019 held a professorship at the Akademie der Bildenden Künste Nürnberg. His books with Steidl include Louis XV (2005), Marc Jacobs Advertising, 1998-2009 (2009), Siegerflieger (2015), The Master IV (2019) and Handbags (2019).

Francesco Bonami and Juergen Teller
50 Times Bonami and Obrist by Teller

Interview by Ewa Hess with Francesco Bonami
Book design by Christoph Radl
112 pages
9 × 11.8 in. / 23 × 30 cm
102 color images
Four-color process
Softcover

€ 35.00 / £ 30.00 / US$ 40.00
ISBN 978-3-95829-643-5

On the occasion of Hans Ulrich Obrist's fiftieth birthday in 2018, Swiss gallery 107 S-chanf asked fellow curator Francesco Bonami to create a celebratory exhibition. Bonami's initial idea was to invite 50 artists to create 50 portraits of Obrist in an ambitious collaborative homage. Yet the idea proved a little too ambitious, and Bonami decided to create the portraits all by himself. The gallery provided him with space and materials, and within just two weeks Bonami's 50 oil paintings were ready—endearing and humorous works, many of which playfully incorporate art figures of the past and present including Edward Hopper, Ai Weiwei and Georg Baselitz.

During the Engadine Art Talks in January 2019 Juergen Teller was invited to view the exhibition "50 Times Obrist by Bonami," and with characteristic spontaneity he photographed Bonami and Obrist before each portrait. This resulting book, with Teller's photos on the left-hand pages and Bonami's paintings on the right, is an unconventional and tongue-in-cheek portrait of a portrait.

To me, Swiss curator Hans Ulrich Obrist is what Campbell's soup was to Andy Warhol. He's the epitome of art, a sculpture, an icon.
Francesco Bonami

FRANCESCO BONAMI / JUERGEN TELLER

50 TIMES BONAMI AND OBRIST BY TELLER

Jackie Nickerson is a British, American-born conceptual documentary photographer and filmmaker.

Kanye West is an artist, producer and designer. He has been named twice by Time magazine as one of the 100 most influential people in the world.

Nickerson and West have worked together since February 2015.

This boxed set collects the first three zines that present Kanye West's YEEZY footwear, apparel and accessories. Dark, atmospheric photographs by Jackie Nickerson make up purely visual works, devoid of any text. The oversized zines are printed on rough, uncoated Kamiko paper with intensely black inks. This boxed set showcases each season's unique aesthetic, while tracing the development of the collections as well as West's ongoing collaboration with Nickerson.

Kanye West
YEEZY Seasons 1,2, 3–4 Zines
Boxed Set

Photos by Jackie Nickerson
Book design by Kanye West and Jackie Nickerson
10.7 x 16.5 in. / 27.3 x 41.9 cm
Four-color process
Three softcovers in a cardboard carry case

Season 1
100 pages
89 color photographs

Season 2
124 pages
95 color photographs

Season 3-4
128 pages
88 color photographs

€ 85.00 / £ 80.00 / US$ 95.00
ISBN 978-3-95829-405-9

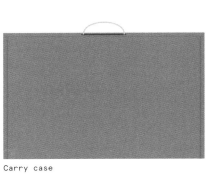
Carry case

Zine 1

Zine 2

Zine 3

Karl Lagerfeld (1938-2019) was a fashion designer, photographer and publisher. Throughout his photographic career Lagerfeld received the Lucky Strike Design Award from the Raymond Loewy Foundation, the cultural prize from the German Photographic Society, and the ICP Trustees Award from the International Center of Photography. Steidl has published most of Lagerfeld's books, including A Portrait of Dorian Gray (2004), Room Service (2006), The Beauty of Violence (2010), The Little Black Jacket (2012), Villa Noailles, Hyères-Été 1995 (2015) and Cassina as seen by Karl (2018).

Choupette is the world's most famous and pampered cat: she has two maids, she receives manicures, and only eats at the table off Goyard and Louis Vuitton crockery. Her Instagram account is approaching an enviable 300,000 followers, and now she has her own brand-new book. *Choupette by Karl Lagerfeld* is a selection of the iPhone photos which Lagerfeld took daily of his beloved pet and muse. Here we see Choupette in a variety of indulgent poses: perched on a pile of books, curled up in the bathroom sink, and (of course) admiring her reflection in the mirror. Lagerfeld personally chose and sequenced these photos, which reveal a tender, playful look into Choupette's precious world.

Choupette has an attitude like a princess ... she knows exactly what she wants. Karl Lagerfeld

You know, personally, I don't even think I'm that famous. Now, Choupette really is famous. She has become the most famous cat in the world. I even get propositioned by pet food companies and things like that, but it's out of the question. I'm commercial. She's not. She's spoiled to death. Obviously. Karl Lagerfeld

Karl Lagerfeld
Choupette by Karl Lagerfeld

Book design by Karl Lagerfeld and Gerhard Steidl
64 pages
5.3 × 8.3 in. / 13.5 × 21 cm
11 black-and-white and 42 color photographs
Four-color process
Clothbound hardcover with a tipped-in photograph

€ 24.00 / £ 20.00 / US$ 30.00
ISBN 978-3-86930-897-5

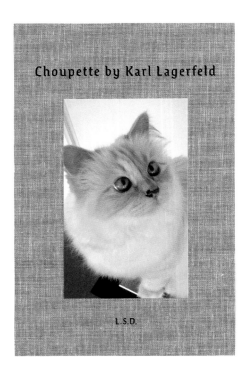

Chanel working on a model for the first collection of her comeback, 1954

Editor-in-chief of Harper's Bazaar UK and
Town & Country UK, Justine Picardie is
an acclaimed journalist and author. Her
books include If the Spirit Moves You
(2001), Wish I May (2004), Daphne (2008)
and Inge Morath: On Style (2016).

This is the long-awaited third edition of Justine Picardie's acclaimed illustrated biography of Coco Chanel (1883–1971), one of the twentieth century's most captivating personalities and a defining figure in fashion history. Whoever attempts to understand Chanel's life is confronted by countless myths, half-truths and rumors. In this book Picardie discovers the woman behind the legend, and tells Chanel's story with a flair and clarity of which Coco herself would approve. *Chanel – Her Life* explores every facet of Chanel's universe: her fascinating private life as well as the famous icons of her fashion empire—the tweed jacket, the little black dress, N° 5 perfume, the pearls, the camellia …

The result is a comprehensive biography that reveals Chanel's style to be the outcome of rigorous elegance, resolute self-belief and a determinedly unconventional stance. Picardie was granted access to Chanel's archives and is the first author to have examined previously undiscovered private archives in the United Kingdom and France; and this unique knowledge underpins *Chanel – Her Life*. The book, designed and with drawings by Karl Lagerfeld, and with a new foreword by Picardie celebrating Lagerfeld's extraordinary time at the House of Chanel, is the definitive biography of the tantalizingly elusive Coco Chanel.

Legend is the consecration of fame. Coco Chanel

Justine Picardie
Chanel – Her Life

Drawings by Karl Lagerfeld
Book Design by Karl Lagerfeld and Gerhard Steidl
400 pages
6.1 x 9.2 in. / 15.5 x 23.4 cm
230 black-and-white and 24 color images
Tritone and four-color process
Clothbound hardcover with dust jacket in a sleeve

€ 58.00 / £ 55.00 / US$ 65.00
ISBN 978-3-95829-630-5

Justine Picardie
Drawings Karl Lagerfeld
Steidl

Born in Kumba in Cameroon in 1962,
Samuel Fosso fled Nigeria and the Biafra
War, and sought refuge in Bangui in the
Central African Republic. He opened his
own commercial photography studio there
at the age of 13. Alongside his portrait
work Fosso began a series of self-
portraits, a mode of representation he
would never abandon. Staging his personal
identity, his work gradually took on a
universal social and political dimension,
as in his celebrated series "Tati" (1997)
and "African Spirits" (2008). Fosso's
work is held in collections such as the
Tate, London; the Musée National d'Art
Moderne, Paris; The Walther Collection,
New York; and the Museum of Modern Art,
New York.

AUTOPORTRAIT is the first comprehensive survey of Samuel Fosso's multifaceted oeuvre. Since the mid-1970s, the artist has focused on self-portraiture and performance, envisioning variations of identity in the postcolonial era. From Fosso's early self-portraits in black-and-white from the 1970s to his recent, continually inventive exercises in self-presentation, highlights include the vibrant series "Tati" (1997), in which he playfully inhabits African and African American characters and archetypes; and the magisterial portraits of "African Spirits" (2008), where he poses as icons of the pan-African liberation and Civil Rights movements, such as Angela Davis, Martin Luther King, Jr., Patrice Lumumba and Nelson Mandela.

This landmark monograph demonstrates Fosso's unique departure from the traditions of West African studio photography, established in the 1950s and '60s by modern masters Seydou Keïta and Malick Sidibé. By charting his conceptual practice of self-portraiture, and sustained engagement with notions of sexuality, gender and self-representation, this book reveals an unprecedented photographic project—one that consistently reflects themes in global visual culture, and covers the range of expressive applications of photography.

Taking pictures is for me a way of liberating myself from the suffering of childhood, from illness, war, everything. I always believed that my life would be pushed aside by other people's, but photography has given me a second life. It's made all lives possible for me.
Samuel Fosso

Co-published with The Walther Collection, New York

Samuel Fosso
AUTOPORTRAIT

Edited by Okwui Enwezor
Foreword by Artur Walther and Jean-Marc Patras
Texts by Quentin Bajac, Yves Chatap, Elvira
Dyangani Ose, Okwui Enwezor, Chika Okeke-Agulu,
Oluremi C. Onabanjo, Terry Smith, Claire Staebler
and James Thomas
Interview by Okwui Enwezor with Samuel Fosso
Book design by Steidl Design
352 pages
9.4 x 11 in. / 24 x 28 cm
87 black-and-white and 101 color photographs
Four color process
Clothbound hardcover with a tipped-in photo

€ 68.00 / £ 50.00 / US$ 75.00
ISBN 978-3-95829-612-1

AUTOPORTRAIT
SAMUEL FOSSO

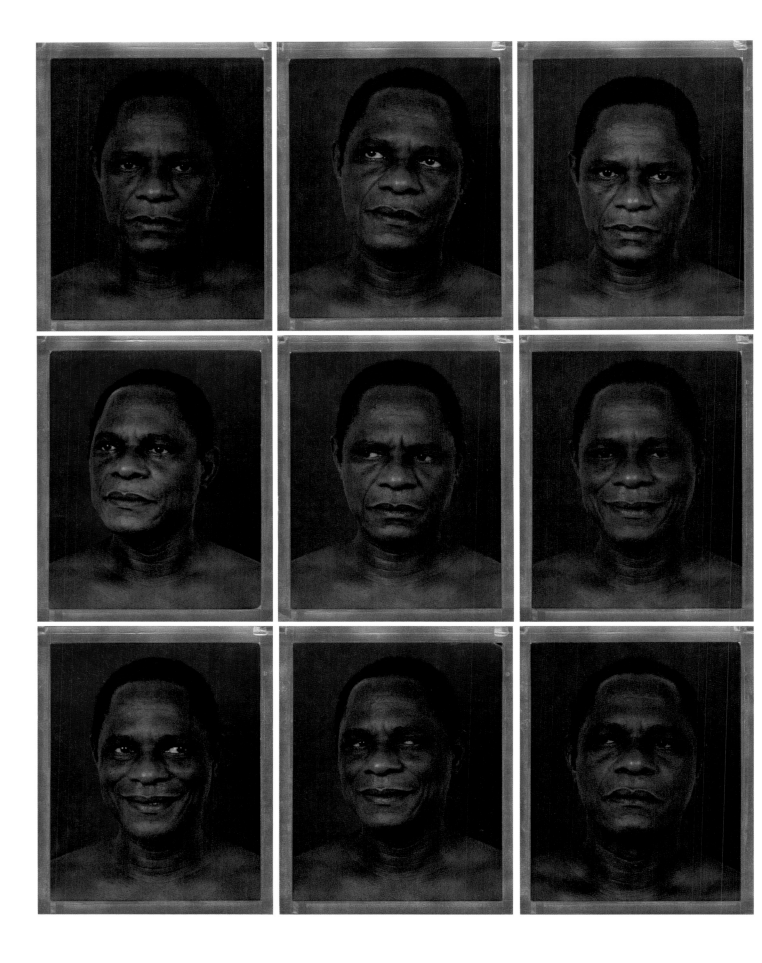

Born in Kumba in Cameroon in 1962, Samuel Fosso fled Nigeria and the Biafra War, and sought refuge in Bangui in the Central African Republic. He opened his own commercial photography studio there at the age of 13. Alongside his portrait work Fosso began a series of self-portraits, a mode of representation he would never abandon. Staging his personal identity, his work gradually took on a universal social and political dimension, as in his celebrated series "TATI" (1997) and "African Spirits" (2008). Fosso's work is held in collections such as the Tate, London; the Musée National d'Art Moderne, Paris; the Walther Collection, Neu-Ulm; and the Museum of Modern Art, New York.

SIXSIXSIX consists of 666 large-format Polaroid self-portraits (each 21.5 × 27 cm), produced in an intensive process by Samuel Fosso with a small team in his Paris studio in 2015 and 2016. Shot against the same rich, colored backdrop, these striking photographs depart from Fosso's earlier self-portraits through their understated and stripped-back approach. Fosso's challenge was to create 666 self-portraits each with a different bodily expression, reminding us of the link between his performances and photography.

In Fosso's words: "In this series there is unhappiness and happiness, misfortune and good fortune. I was very inspired by these two aspects. *SIXSIXSIX* refers to the number of misfortune. By that I mean in terms of what I've encountered in my life up to now. After my illness came the Biafra War; millions of people died, and I was fortunate to be saved. I went to the Central African Republic where I experienced the conflicts of 2014, in which I also could have died. [...] For all that I've been through, God has been with me and saved me. [...] In the end, it's about buried emotions that we ourselves create, and about exorcizing my own resentment in the face of this situation. From 1976 to 2014, I have never been at peace in my life when faced with the actions of those who always sow misfortune among children and innocents."

When I work, it's always a performance that I choose to undertake. It's not a subject or an object; it's one more human being.
Samuel Fosso

Samuel Fosso
SIXSIXSIX

Text by Hans Ulrich Obrist
Foreword Jean Marc Patras
Book design by Steidl Design
684 pages
7.4 x 9.4 in. / 19 x 24 cm
666 color photographs
Hardcover

€ 85.00 / £ 78.00 / US$ 95.00
ISBN 978-3-95829-509-4

In this book Sebastian Posingis photographs the famed Sri Lankan garden of architect Geoffrey Bawa (1919–2003), described by its creator as a "place of many moods, the result of many imaginings." In 1948, as Ceylon was slipping off the shackles of colonial rule, the then young reluctant lawyer Bawa returned home from a decade of study and travel, and bought an abandoned rubber estate near the town of Bentota. He renamed it "Lunuganga" or "Salt River," and set out to transform it into a tropical evocation of the great landscape gardens of England and Italy that he had explored during his travels.

50 years later the garden was in its prime and had taken on a life of its own. Great trees had been felled and new ones planted to create it, hills had been moved and terraces cut, and now artworks graced it as objects for contemplation. And yet the garden seemed so natural that it belied the effort of its creation; it was a manicured wilderness of green on green, a place of unfolding vistas and rhythms. Today the garden survives, miraculously and precariously; and now within the pages of this book.

This collection of images does not pretend to describe a real garden. It is a dream, a fleeting memory: one individual's subjective response to an imagined place at a particular moment in time; a tribute to an idea and the man who conceived it. David Robson

Sebastian Posingis
Salt River

Text by David Robson
Book design by Sebastian Posingis
and Gerhard Steidl
88 pages
9.4 × 13 in. / 24 × 33 cm
50 black-and-white photographs
Tritone
Clothbound hardcover

€ 65.00 / £ 60.00 / US$ 75.00
ISBN 978-3-95829-620-6

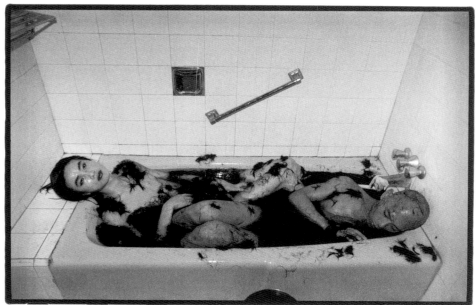

RongRong was born in Fujian Province, China, in 1968. He was a key member of the Beijing East Village group, experimenting with photography and documenting the performances of his fellow artists in the early 1990s, which have attained an almost mythic status in the history of contemporary Chinese experimental art. In 2006 RongRong and his wife inri founded Three Shadows Photography Art Centre, emphasizing international collaborations and the creation of a sustainable infrastructure for young Chinese artists. His work has been exhibited worldwide over three decades, and is held in the collections of the Museum of Modern Art, New York; the Getty Museum, Los Angeles; the Myriam and Guy Ullens Foundation, Beijing; the Mori Art Museum, Tokyo; and several distinguished private foundations.

This book presents an expansive selection of striking photographs, together with first-person accounts from his private diary, which RongRong made between 1993 and 1998 within the artistic community known as Beijing East Village—now poignantly described as "a meteor in the history of contemporary Chinese art." RongRong's acutely composed and richly expressive images captured scenes of daily life among fellow young, aspiring artists, and created now definitive documents of iconic performance works by Zhang Huan and Ma Liuming, among others. Often highly challenging works, their performances and photographs would send an instant shockwave throughout the Chinese avant-garde, and later the global art scene. Revisiting these texts and images anew on the occasion of this publication, RongRong has composed an absorbing personal narrative of an artist coming into his own. *RongRong's Diary. Beijing East Village* also serves as an invaluable, first-hand record of a burgeoning artistic community, its precarious political context, and the real lives behind a pivotal moment in Chinese contemporary art.

But here in the East Village, we do almost everything. Curse plays rock music and writes poetry. Kongbu curates and writes criticism. Zhang Huan, Ma Liuming and Zhu Ming do performances... But I am the only photographer. Forming a complete collective, we must be able to make meaningful works... Everyone left their hometown and seeks dreams here from afar. We are all children who left home, which makes us constantly hungry... RongRong

Co-published with The Walther Collection, New York, and Three Shadows Photography Art Centre

RongRong
RongRong's Diary
Beijing East Village

Texts by RongRong and Silvia Fok
Afterword by Artur Walther and Christopher Phillips
Book design by Paloma Tarrio Alves / Steidl Design
248 pages
8.3 × 10.2 in. / 21 × 26 cm
124 black-and-white images
Tritone process
Clothbound hardcover with a tipped-in photograph

€ 48.00 / £ 45.00 / US$ 60.00
ISBN 978-3-95829-592-6

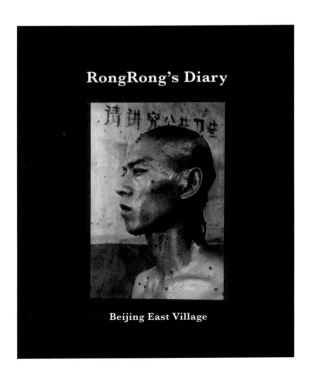

Charles H. Traub has been photographing
for 50 years, with more than a dozen books
published of his pictures and writings.
Traub was instrumental in establishing
the Museum of Contemporary Photography in
Chicago, was director of the prestigious
Light Gallery in New York, and president
of the Aaron Siskind Foundation. His
photographs have been widely exhibited
and are held in major collections
worldwide. Throughout his career, Traub
has been a leading educator in the
photographic arts. He founded the graduate
photography program at the School of
Visual Arts in New York City and has been
its chair for 30 years.

These on-the-spot portraits of "the fallen" were taken to reveal the
dignity and unexamined humanity of those who were once intrinsic
to the urban experience of American cities of the late 1970s. In
Charles H. Traub's own words: "It is my hope that these photographs
of the tenants of the streets of Uptown Chicago and the Bowery New
York serve as a tribute to the grace of the 'down and out.'" And from
Tom Huhn's essay in the book: "What a curious thing to look at, and
to look for: whatever there is in each of us—by spying what might be
found missing in someone else."

Indifference and gentrification have displaced those who once
inhabited the missions and shelters that nurtured and held them
together in a storied bond. While homeless, they were not wayward;
they formed a fabled tribe and were known to their neighbors by their
names, eccentricities and their plight. Nelson Algren's famous book
A Walk on the Wild Side asks why "lost people sometimes develop to
greater human beings than those who have never been lost in their
lives." Traub's *Skid Row* confirms this and these inhabitants' part in
the central fabric of the city.

*No bromides, no armchair humanism: in these photographs Charles
Traub displays the difficult ethic of the street portrait. He captures his
subjects sometimes with their cooperation, sometimes even against
their will, but always in pursuit of an urgent goal—to bring the margin
to the center, to acknowledge "them" as us. Where is so-called Skid
Row? Wherever people have lost a grip on economic reality and with
it their status as human beings.* Lyle Rexer

Charles H. Traub
Skid Row

Texts by Tom Huhn and Charles H. Traub
Book design by Yoav Friedländer
112 pages
9.2 × 10.5 in. / 23.4 × 26.7 cm
51 black-and-white photographs
Tritone
Clothbound hardcover

€ 35.00 / £ 30.00 / US$ 40.00
ISBN 978-3-95829-625-1

Born in 1966, Kai Wiedenhöfer studied
photography at the Folkwang University
of the Arts in Essen and Arabic in
Damascus. He is the recipient of the
Leica Medal of Excellence, numerous World
Press Photo Awards, the Eugene Smith
Grant and the Carmignac Gestion Award.
Wiedenhöfer's books with Steidl include
The Book of Destruction (2010), published
for an exhibition at the Musée d'Art
Moderne Paris; and Confrontier (2013),
documenting separation walls and displayed
in "WALLonWALL" on the Berlin Wall. In
2016 this exhibition was succeeded by
"WARonWALL," depicting the war in Syria.
In 2016 Wiedenhöfer received the Carl von
Ossietzky Medal from the International
Human Rights League.

"Good fences make good neighbors"—so goes the proverb. But what makes a good fence? Certainly not one that prevents neighbors from being seen in the first place. Indeed, such divisive barriers create enemies. Peace starts where walls fall, not where they are erected. The Berlin Wall is the best proof of that, says Kai Wiedenhöfer, who witnessed its fall first hand. Wiedenhöfer has photographed separation barriers throughout the world, from Berlin in 1989, to Belfast, Mexico, Ceuta and Melilla, Baghdad—and frequently in Israel, to document the walls with which the country has so comprehensively surrounded itself: at the borders to the West Bank, the Gaza Strip, Egypt and Lebanon. Between 2003 and 2018 he made ten journeys to Israel and the Occupied Palestinian Territories to photograph the fences, walls and checkpoints which the Israeli government is still building.

Wiedenhöfer has documented the Israeli-Palestinian conflict over three decades now. His new photos show that the hope of lasting peace in the region is becoming ever more unrealistic in our time. For a wall is a paradox: it intensifies the very violence it seeks to keep in check, and thereby makes further surveillance and fortifications necessary.

A barrier is a proof of our weaknesses and error, of the inability of human beings to communicate with each other. Where all communication is contracted, a solution of conflicts becomes impossible because behind walls the clichés and concepts of the enemy mushroom with hardly any relation to reality. Kai Wiedenhöfer

Kai Wiedenhöfer
WALL and PEACE

Text by Kai Wiedenhöfer
Book design by Dirk Fütterer
208 pages
14.9 x 11.9 in. / 38 x 30.4 cm
24 black-and-white and 67 color photographs
Tritone and four-color process
Clothbound hardcover

€ 98.00 / £ 90.00 / US$ 125.00
ISBN 978-3-95829-571-1

Born in 1971, Donovan Wylie is a
photographer and filmmaker based in his
native Belfast. Exploring alternative
strategies for the representation of
conflict, Wylie combines conceptual and
typological approaches, and asks us to
consider the role of photography within
the contexts of preservation, memory and
history. Wylie is Professor of Photography
at Ulster University, and his work is
held in numerous public collections
including the Metropolitan Museum of
Art, New York; the Yale University Art
Gallery, New Haven; and the Irish Museum
of Modern Art, Dublin. Wylie's books with
Steidl include Maze (2009), Outposts
(2011), North Warning System (2014) and
Housing Plans for the Future (2018).

Chris Klatell is a writer and lawyer
based in New York. He writes frequently
about photography, including recent
collaborations with Donovan Wylie (A Good
and Spacious Land, 2017), Jim Goldberg
(Candy, 2017), Gilles Peress (Annals
of the North, 2019) and Zoe Strauss
(Commencement, 2019).

Through photographing singular lighthouses as seen from the opposing coastlines of France and the home nations of the United Kingdom, Belfast-based artist Donovan Wylie confronts the physical barriers and invitations to crossing created by the sea.

Immediately following the June 2016 referendum, Wylie began exploring ideas of family dynamics and fractured relationships as a way to understand the United Kingdom's current state. In collaboration with the writer Chris Klatell and the Seamus Heaney Centre, this project responds to Virginia Woolf's *To the Lighthouse* (1927), which investigates the complexities of seeing, loss and the passage of time. By photographing the afterglow of distant lighthouses to process the tensions and complexities of identity and isolationism, *Lighthouse* simultaneously represents closeness and distance, interrogating how the isolation of the British landscape contributes to understanding our national identity.

We mostly picture lighthouses in their useless state: unlit, during the day, quaint, obsolete. At dusk, across the water, they come to life—an inscrutable flash, both coming and going, marking time and distance. We wait for that light as we anticipate a lover or an invader, and then ask with Woolf's James Ramsey: "So that was the Lighthouse, was it? No, the other was also the Lighthouse. For nothing was simply one thing." Chris Klatell

Donovan Wylie and Chris Klatell
Lighthouse

Photographs by Donovan Wylie
Text by Chris Klatell
Book design by Donovan Wylie, Bernard Fischer
and Gerhard Steidl
80 pages
11.6 × 9.1 in. / 29.5 × 23 cm
21 black-and-white photographs
Four-color process
Clothbound hardcover with dust jacket

€ 40.00 / £ 35.00 / US$ 45.00
ISBN 978-3-95829-639-8

Harf Zimmermann was born in 1955 in Dresden, and in 1961 moved to Berlin where he today lives and works. After initially training as a journalist, Zimmermann studied photography under Arno Fischer at the Academy of Fine Arts in Leipzig. He was a founding member of the photographic agency Ostkreuz, and today contributes to a range of international magazines. Steidl has published Zimmermann's Brand Wand (2015) and Hufelandstraße 1055 Berlin (2017).

In *The Sad-Eyed Lady* Harf Zimmermann documents the Berliner Luft- und Badeparadies ("Blub" for short), a once loved bathing and leisure center in the Britz district of Berlin that is today a graffiti-stained ruin. The center opened in 1985 at an impressive cost of 44 million marks and welcomed roughly seven million visitors before its closure in 2005 after a series of hygiene complaints. Zimmerman's focus is the center's slow death, the eerie remnants of pleasure that once was. In his words: "The city has been left behind and the silence is near complete. All the bridges are broken, the windows nailed over or opaque with dirt—everything here appears bewitched. This could be the realm of the Snow Queen, where the beautiful princess is imprisoned, trapped by an evil spell. Or it could be the Star Trek episode where Captain Kirk beams himself onto a celestial body with Bones and Spock after his sensors register signs of life, only to realize that the aliens have left their planet or been killed before they could escape. And now no one can know how they looked, those beings, and what purpose the strange objects they left behind may have served."

There are many ways of perceiving the world, but I am obsessed by those aspects that go unnoticed by most. Harf Zimmermann

Harf Zimmermann
The Sad-Eyed Lady

Text by Harf Zimmermann
Book design by Harf Zimmermann and Steidl Design
136 pages
12 × 14.6 in. / 30.5 × 37 cm
68 color photographs
Four-color process
Clothbound hardcover in a slipcase

€ 58.00 / £ 50.00 / US$ 65.00
ISBN 978-3-95829-605-3

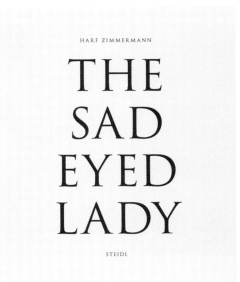

Slipcase

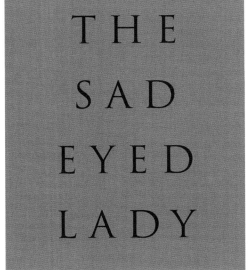

Book

Born in a secret city, a nuclear research center in the Urals, Gleb Kosorukov moved to Moscow after completing school. There he continued his studies at the National Research Nuclear University MEPhI, where he attained a master's degree in nuclear physics. Directly after graduation he started a career in photography, contributing to publications including the New York Times, The Guardian and Time. Then moving to Paris, he drifted towards artistic practice, while making commercial work for Russian Vogue, i-D, GQ and Elle, among others. His recent years have been devoted mostly to personal projects. Kosorukov's works are held in the Moscow Multimedia Art Museum, the State Russian Museum, the Museum of Moscow, and the State Hermitage. Steidl published Kosorukov's Heroes of Labour in 2018.

Samasthiti—Sanskrit for "returning to the original balanced state"

The concept of this book is to blend together two formally independent sequences of images, shot over a period of two months. The first sequence is part of a larger body of work taken in the area of conflict in Eastern Ukraine. It comprises images of urban destruction caused by heavy bombardment that are presented here in the order the shots were taken. The second sequence was made in Paris, providing technical images for an Ashtanga Yoga book published by teachers Gérald Disse and Linda Munro. This sequence is similarly strictly arranged, in the order the images were presented in the draft layout of the yoga book. The intentionally mechanical combination of these two unmanaged and independent sequences produces multiple new narratives for the viewer to interpret. Kosorukov's *Smasthiti* serves as a metaphor for the new reality which he believes we are currently slowly drifting towards.

Mapping reality allows us to look into the future. Hans Ulrich Obrist

Gleb Kosorukov
Samasthiti

Text by Gleb Kosorukov
Book design by Gleb Kosorukov and Gerhard Steidl
440 pages
11.8 × 7.9 in. / 30 × 20 cm
428 color photographs
Four-color process
Softcover

€ 50.00 / £ 45.00 / US$ 60.00
ISBN 978-3-95829-631-2

Born in Göttingen in 1973, Christian Lesemann today lives and works in Berlin. His photography has been published in a variety of magazines and books, including Dazed & Confused, ZEITmagazin and 100 Years of Swiss Graphic Design. Lesemann has participated in exhibitions at the Centre Pompidou and Schirn Kunsthalle Frankfurt, among other institutions.

Christian Lesemann had to unlearn a certain kind of photography in order to take the pictures of parked cars in this book—to unlearn how to compose his shots, to unlearn how to find the right light, to unlearn how to select and edit. "It took me a year to find the randomness I was looking for," Lesemann explains. It took another four or five years for him to build a body of work large enough to achieve his desired effect.

This sensation is one of being overwhelmed by the banality of his chosen subject, created by the sheer volume of photos rather than the distinction of any individual image. The more we look, the more bored we become; the more bored we become, the greater our chances of breaking through to discover what lies on the other side. For Lesemann, casting aside his training and intuition required a leap of faith. As viewers, confronted with photos lacking any traditional "merit," take a similar leap. The outcome might be an existential insight, a heightened awareness or a new sense wonderment, but there's no guarantee. In the end, all we have for certain is a book of photos of parked cars—and really, can we even be sure of that?

I have no idea what these photos are about, but they're somehow just good. Ole Petscheleit

Christian Lesemann
Parked

Text by Alex Marashian
Book design by Gerhard Steidl
176 pages
11.7 x 9.1 in. / 29.8 x 23.2 cm
163 color photographs
Four-color process
Clothbound hardcover with dust jacket

€ 50.00 / £ 45.00 / US$ 60.00
ISBN 978-3-95829-617-6

10

11

nicht was man sieht, sondern wie man sieht ...

Dr. Paul Wolff, 1933–34

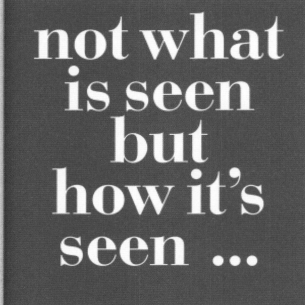

not what is seen but how it's seen ...

26

27

The medical doctor Paul Wolff (1887-1951) began his photographic career in Frankfurt am Main during the Weimar Republic. In time he became one of the most important representatives of the small-format Leica camera, whose functions he conveyed to the amateur in his many iconic photographic manuals. Together with his business partner Alfred Tritschler (1905-70) Wolff established one of the largest photo studios in Germany; through the wide dissemination of their pictures they left a lasting impact on the history of the German photobook.

Manfred Heiting has been a collector, curator, designer and editor of photography and photo publications since the 1970s. Books edited and designed by Heiting at Steidl include Autopsie, German-language Photobooks, 1918-1945 (2012 and 2014, together with Roland Jaeger), The Soviet Photobook, 1920-1941 (2015), The Japanese Photobook, 1912-1990 (2017) and Czech and Slovak Photo Publications, 1918-1989 (2018). He is also planning The Dutch Photobook, 1918-1990.

Born in 1987, Kristina Lemke studied art history and German literature in Marburg and Mainz. Her dissertation explores the continuities and tendencies in Paul Wolff's work. Lemke works as a curator and researcher in the photographic department of the Städel Museum in Frankfurt, and has contributed to the exhibitions Lichtbilder (2014), Geschlechterkampf (2017) and Lotte Laserstein (2018).

This book presents the photo publications of Dr. Paul Wolff and Alfred Tritschler, revealing both their extensive artistic skills and business acumen. Wolff and Tritschler's versatile approach encompassed industrial reportages, genre pictures, news coverage, advertising campaigns and even films. In this volume, their more than 1,000 known published works and many magazine contributions are gathered and illustrated in color for the first time. Texts drawing on extensive primary sources explore Wolff and Tritschler's most important creations and reconstruct the history of their company.

We see just how markedly the contexts for the production and consumption of photography changed between the Weimar Republic and Third Reich, and how Wolff and Tritschler exemplify the pivotal role which outstanding individuals played within this history. Their journalistic activities developed within the larger expansion of photographic illustration; their success was closely linked to the advancement of media reception and its use in political policies. Wolff and Tritschler's photo publications take on a further, political meaning—also in terms of National Socialist ideology—in the context of their concrete usage. This book's focus on their entire oeuvre, particularly the little seen early and late output, makes it the most comprehensive evaluation of Wolff and Tritschler's multifaceted work to date.

Not what is seen but how it's seen. Dr. Paul Wolff

Manfred Heiting (ed.)
Dr. Paul Wolff & Alfred Tritschler
Publications 1906—2019

Bilingual edition (English / German)
Edited and book design by Manfred Heiting
Introduction by Manfred Heiting
Text by Kristina Lemke
Essays by Rainer Stamm and Ed Schwartzreich
520 pages
10.7 x 11.5 in. / 27.1 x 29.3 cm
2,300 color illustrations
Four-color process
Hardcover

€ 95.00 / £ 85.00 / US$ 125.00
ISBN 978-3-95829-614-5

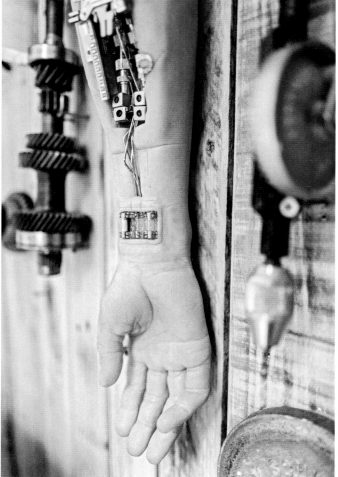

Hans Georg Näder was born in 1961 in Duderstadt to Maria Näder (née Bock) and Max Näder. Näder studied business administration and assumed control of Ottobock with approximately 1,000 employees at the age of 28. Under his leadership the company has become the world market leader in prosthetics, and major milestones such as the first microprocessor-controlled leg prosthesis C-Leg have been launched.

For generations, world-leading German prosthetics company Ottobock has been restoring mobility to people and developing wearable human bionics to mobilize the human body. Published on the centenary of Ottobock, this book presents the vision for the future of human mobility of Hans Georg Näder, chairman of the company and grandson of its founder.

What roles will digitalization, robotics, prostheses, artificial intelligence and the imagination play in how we optimize and employ our bodies, and shape the development of humanity? With photos by Christoph Neumann, and conceived and realized by Thomas Huber, *Futuring Human Mobility* explores these questions and their philosophical, ethical, social, political, economic and medical implications in our changing and diverse global community. Incorporating interviews, essays, short stories and artwork by 40 international experts including David Chipperfield, Philipp Craven, EVA & ADELE, Yuval Noah Harari, Hugh Herr, Hiroshi Ishiguro, Chandran Nair, Carsten Nicolai, Neo Rauch, Wolfgang Schäuble, Kevin Warwick and Ranga Yogeshwar, the book is a fountain of inspiration and a call for us to look beyond the narrow horizon of the present to a future of dynamic possibilities.

We're standing on the threshold of a new age in which digitalization, the rapid rise of artificial intelligence and the triumphant advance of robots promise a new long wave of growth and prosperity, while simultaneously raising the fundamental question of what constitutes the essential core of human existence. Hans Georg Näder

Hans Georg Näder
Futuring Human Mobility

Photos by Christoph Neumann
Concept and realization by Thomas Huber
Illustrations by John Hathway and Daniel Ramirez Pérez
Texts by Mariacarla Gadebusch Bondio, Heike Fuhlbrügge, Peter Glaser, Yuval Noah Harari, Eckart von Hirschhausen, Thomas Huber, Hans Georg Näder, Julia Näder, Helga Nowotny, Wolfgang Schäuble, Mark C. Schneider, Gerhard Steidl and Stefan Thurner
Interviews with Sonia Blandford, Dorothee Blessing, David Chipperfield, Philip Craven, Hans Dietl, Axel Ekkernkamp, EVA & ADELE, Jenny Lay-Flurrie, Dietrich Grönemeyer, Stefan W. Hell, Hugh Herr, Hiroshi Ishiguro, Peter Kägi, Catrin Misselhorn, Georgia Näder, Chandran Nair, Carsten Nicolai, Sophie de Oliveira Barata, Heinrich Popow, Neo Rauch, Martine Rothblatt, Doug Saunders, Michael Schäfer, Philipp Thesen, Gorden Wagener, Kevin Warwick and Ranga Yogeshwar
Book design by Gerhard Steidl and Holger Feroudj
264 pages
8.5 × 11.3 in. / 21.5 × 28.5 cm
60 black-and-white and 140 color images
Four-color process
Clothbound hardcover

€ 25.00 / £ 20.00 / US$ 30.00
ISBN 978-3-95829-635-0

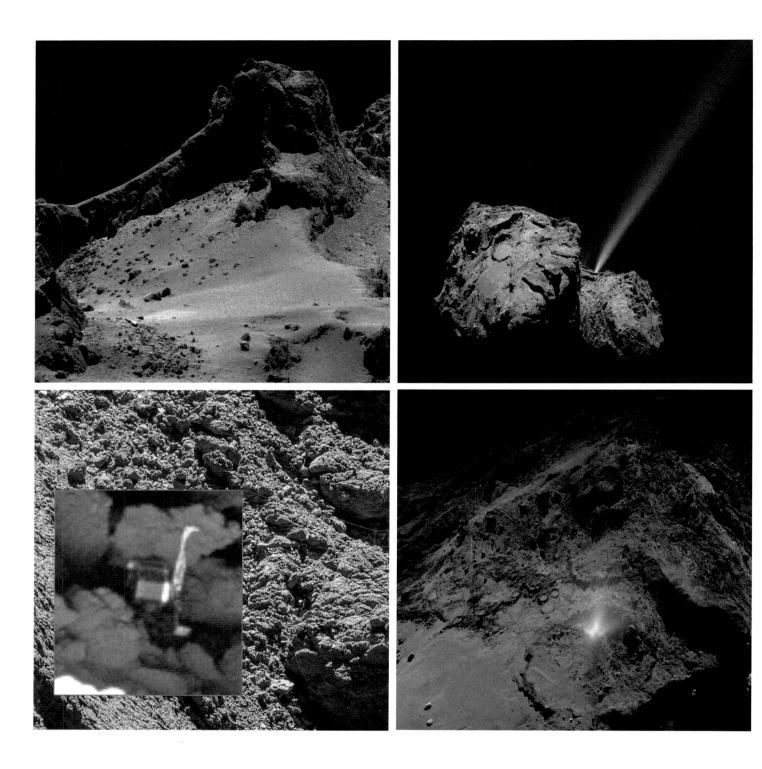

Holger Sierks, Carsten Güttler and Cecilia
Tubiana of the Max Planck Institute
for Solar System Research in Göttingen
represent the team of scientists and
engineers that built and operated OSIRIS.
It took more than 30 years of planning,
construction and travel for OSIRIS to
finally reach comet 67P.

Comets as beautiful phenomena in the night sky have fascinated humans and inspired our imagination for millennia. Having witnessed the formation of our solar system 4.6 billion years ago, comets are also a scientist's dream to study. Composed of fluffy dust, several ices and rich organics, it has long been believed that they preserve pristine material from this early time and therefore hold the key to understanding the origin of the solar system with all its planets—and ultimately life. To make this dream a reality, the Rosetta mission visited a comet named 67P/Churyumov-Gerasimenko between 2014 and 2016. On board the orbiting Rosetta spacecraft were eleven scientific instruments as well as Philae, an in situ laboratory to land on the comet's surface. The camera system OSIRIS (Optical, Spectroscopic and Infrared Remote Imaging System) can certainly be considered the "Eyes of Rosetta."

This book collects the most stunning images acquired by OSIRIS and compiled by the scientists who were responsible for the development and operation of the camera system. From the launch of the Rosetta spacecraft on board an Ariane 5 rocket, to a journey through space of more than ten years to reach 67P/Churyumov-Gerasimenko, *OSIRIS – The Eyes of Rosetta* allows us to explore a comet with our own eyes and discover how exotic yet oddly familiar it is.

Exhibition: Kunsthaus Göttingen, 2021

Holger Sierks, Carsten Güttler and Cecilia Tubiana (eds.)
OSIRIS – The Eyes of Rosetta
Journey to Comet 67P, a Witness to the Birth of Our Solar System

Texts by Holger Sierks, Carsten Güttler
and Cecilia Tubiana
Book design by Steidl Design
328 pages
11.8 × 11.8 in. / 30 × 30 cm
245 black-and-white and 11 color photographs
Tritone process
Hardcover

€ 75.00 / £ 70.00 / US$ 85.00
ISBN 978-3-95829-622-0

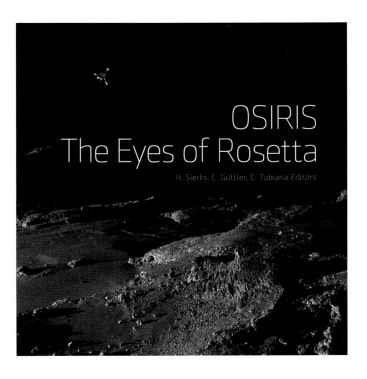

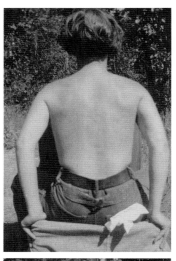
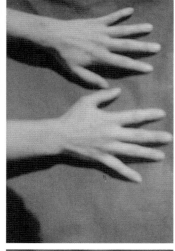

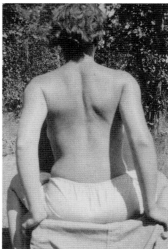

Imagining Everyday Life evolved from a
two-day symposium at Columbia University
in October 2018—a collaboration between
The Walther Collection, Barnard's Center
for Research on Women, and the Center
for the Study of Social Difference at
Columbia University. This publication
unfolds in four parts: Why Vernacular
Photography? The Limits and Possibilities
of A Field; Troubling Portraiture:
Photographic Portraits and The Shadow
Archive; Performance and Transformation:
Photographic (Re)visions of Subjectivity;
and Space, Materiality, and the Social
Worlds of the Photograph.

Tina Campt, Marianne Hirsch,
Gil Hochberg and Brian Wallis (eds.)
Imagining Everyday Life: Engagements
with Vernacular Photography

Texts by Ariella Azoulay, Geoffrey Batchen, Ali
Behdad, Elspeth Brown, Clément Chéroux, Lily Cho,
Nicole Fleetwood, Sophie Hackett, Patricia Hayes,
Barbara Kirshenblatt-Gimblett, Thy Phu, Leigh Raiford,
Shawn Michelle Smith, Drew Thompson, Laura Wexler and
Deborah Willis
Book design by Steidl Design
400 pages
6.7 × 9.7 in. / 17 × 24.5 cm
180 black-and-white and 180 color images
Four-color process
Softcover

€ 65.00 / £ 60.00 / US$ 75.00
ISBN 978-3-95829-627-5

Imagining Everyday Life: Engagements with Vernacular Photography
surveys the expansive field of vernacular photography, the vast archive
of utilitarian images created for bureaucratic structures, commercial
usage and personal commemoration, as opposed to elite aesthetic
purposes. As a crucial extension of its ongoing investigation of vernacular photography, The Walther Collection has collaborated with key
scholars and critical thinkers in the history of photography, women's
studies, queer theory, Africana studies and curatorial practice to
interrogate vernacular's theoretical limits, as well as to conduct
case studies of a striking array of objects and images, many from the
collection's holdings.

From identification portraits of California migrant workers, phy-
sique photographs that circulated underground in queer communities,
to one-of-a-kind commemorative military albums from Louisiana to
Vietnam, these richly illustrated essays treat a breadth of material
formats, social uses and shared communities, offering new ways to
consider photography in relation to our political affiliations, personal
agency and daily rituals. By reconsidering the multiple contexts and
meanings of often-overlooked photographic practices, *Imagining
Everyday Life* is a groundbreaking contribution—articulating the vital
debates and complexities within an energizing new field.

*It is critical in thinking about vernacular photography and the history
of photography to recuperate or salvage objects whose backstories
have often been lost or curtailed. These vernacular photographs are
documents of social histories that would not otherwise be explored;
they are key historical artifacts of suppressed or oppressed lives, and
studying them is a way to reanimate their histories.* Brian Wallis

Co-published with The Walther Collection, New York

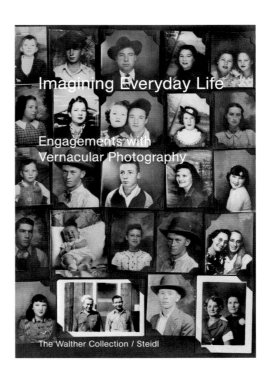

Henri Lustiger Thaler is chief curator of
the Amud Aish Memorial Museum in Brooklyn,
Professor of Historical Sociology at
Ramapo College of New Jersey, and Research
Associate of the École des Hautes Études
en Sciences Sociales in Paris. Lustiger
Thaler is a writer, filmmaker and the
director of the Orthodox Testimony Project
at the United States Holocaust Memorial
Museum in Washington. His exhibition
work has appeared internationally and
he is the author and editor of seven
books, most recently Witnessing Unbound:
Holocaust Representation and the Origins
of Memory (2017).

Born in Florida in 1954, documentary and
portrait photographer Caryl Englander
lives and works in New York, where she
is Chair of the International Center of
Photography. In 1993 Englander gained
a masters of photography from the dual
program of New York University and the
International Center of Photography. She
has created portraits for and taught at
the Jewish Community Center in Manhattan,
and her exhibitions include "Acts of
Charity, Deeds of Kindness" for the
Metropolitan Council on Jewish Poverty in
2005, comprising photo-essays exploring
the varied humanitarian functions of the
council.

Polish-American architect Daniel
Libeskind is an international figure in
architecture and urban design who aims to
create work that is resonant, original
and sustainable. Libeskind established his
architecture studio in Berlin in 1989,
after winning the competition to build
the city's Jewish Museum. In February
2003 Studio Libeskind moved from Berlin
to New York to oversee the master plan
for the World Trade Center redevelopment
in Lower Manhattan. Libeskind's practice
involves designing and realizing a diverse
array of urban, cultural and commercial
projects worldwide.

Henri Lustiger Thaler,
Caryl Englander,
Daniel Libeskind
Through the Lens of Faith
Auschwitz

Photographs by Caryl Englander
Essay by Henri Lustiger Thaler
Book design by Paloma Tarrio Alves
and Gerhard Steidl
64 pages
6.9 × 9.4 in. / 17.5 x 24 cm
28 color photographs
Four-color process
Softcover

€ 24.00 / £ 20.00 / US$ 30.00
ISBN 978-3-95829-654-1

Through the Lens of Faith is Caryl Englander's original and affecting visual archive of witnesses of the Holocaust, presented alongside conversations exploring their diverse belief systems. Englander's subjects are between the ages of 80 and 102, and she photographed them during emotive moments of interviewing over the past three years. The resulting portraits encapsulate mnemonic tensions between an unmasterable past and the present.

Englander photographed intense discursive encounters during which writer Henri Lustiger Thaler, chief curator of the Amud Aish Memorial Museum, who has interviewed hundreds of Holocaust survivors, asked Englander's subjects to share their stories of Auschwitz, centering on the question of faith: how did it express itself in an environment that was its complete antithesis? Lustiger Thaler's careful arrangement of the survivors' voices presents their complex spiritual responses and narrates the brutality of everyday life in the concentration camp. In his own words: "We present stories that are very different from epic-like narratives of 'spiritual resistance.' We engage everyday accounts of life in Auschwitz-Birkenau, where faith functioned as a human anchor, a touchstone for expressions of identity and longings for freedom."

Through the Lens of Faith will furthermore be realized as an exhibition designed by Daniel Libeskind, the renowned architect of memorial spaces including Berlin's Jewish Museum. Opening on 1 July 2019 at the Auschwitz-Birkenau Museum Memorial site and displayed for the entire 75th commemorative year (2020) of the liberation of the camp, the exhibition is estimated to be seen by approximately 4 million visitors. Libeskind's moving design juxtaposes Englander's photos against the visceral entry to Auschwitz, creating confrontation between symbols of imprisonment and freedom.

My work is a visual testament to the absolute endurance of human courage. With each person I had the privilege to meet, I felt their resilience, their hope and their joy for life. Caryl Englander

Exhibition: Auschwitz-Birkenau Museum Memorial, Poland, July 2019 to December 2020

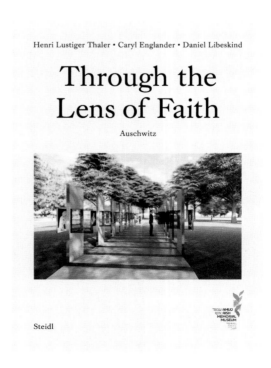

Henri Lustiger Thaler • Caryl Englander • Daniel Libeskind

Through the Lens of Faith

Auschwitz

Steidl

Ed Clark

William Eggleston

David Freund

Lee Friedlander

Bruce Davidson

Frank Gohlke

Henry Wessel

Mary Ellen Mark

John Cohen

Jeff Brouws

Anders Petersen

Gunnar Smoliansky

Christer Strömholm

Ed Kashi

Yves Marchand

Romain Meffre

Ken Light

Shelby Lee Adams

Liu Zheng

Ernst Haas

Angela Grauerholz

Lucida Devlin

Mauro D'Agati

François-Marie Banier

Langdon Clay

Paul Drake

Helen File

Guido Mocafico

Sze Tsung Nicolás Leong

Sheva Fruitman

Andy Summers

Marq Sutherland

Koto Bolofo

Anish Kapoor

Tomi Ungerer

Roni Horn

Hannah Collins

Previously announced

We love that the experience of a photobook is a slow one. To best savor its meanings as pictured by the artist, you need to take a book in your hands and unhurriedly turn each page—not just to scrutinize the photos and the cumulative sequence they form, but to register the touch of the paper and cover, and to inhale the scent of ink on paper.

Making books as we like them can be a slow process too. And we admit that sometimes their creation can take a little longer than first thought. Perhaps a book's concept has changed or been entirely rethought. Perhaps the inspiration needs space to grow. Perhaps new photos are discovered during the editing process, or we choose a bespoke paper with a long production time.

We welcome all these adventures, and give each book the time it needs. We hope you find it well worth the wait, and remember: Slow is the New Fast!

LIFE

PARIS: 1946

MARCH 18, 1946 **10** CENTS
YEARLY SUBSCRIPTION $4.50

Born in 1911 in Nashville, Tennessee, was a quintessential and prolific American photojournalist. Clark began assisting staff photographers at the daily Nashville Tennessean in 1929, and worked for the paper until 1942. He was hired as a stringer for Life in 1936, the publication's inaugural year, and began his long tenure as a full-time Life staff photographer in 1942. In his work for Life over the next 20 years, Clark held posts in Nashville, Paris, Moscow, London, Hollywood and Washington, D.C. He received a wide range of assignments, from political figures and events, to Hollywood's celebrities, to charming human interest stories. Working in both the United States and Europe, Clark covered some of the most important subjects of his time, including the post-war rebuilding of Germany and France and the desegregation of schools in Arkansas. In 1962 he was forced to leave Life due to failing eyesight, yet in 1980 advances in ocular surgery restored Clark's vision and he returned to making photographs in later years. He died in 2000 at the age of 88. Today Clark's archive is held by the Meserve-Kunhardt Foundation in Pleasantville, New York.

Ed Clark
On Assignment
1931–1962

Edited by Keith F. Davis and Peter W. Kunhardt, Jr.
Text by Keith F. Davis
Book design by Duncan Whyte, Gerhard Steidl and Peter W. Kunhardt, Jr.
9.8 x 11.4 in. / 25 x 29 cm

Vol. 1: Plates and illustrated timeline
344 pages
319 black-and-white and 18 color photographs

Vol. 2: Personal scrapbooks
328 pages
161 color images

Tritone and four-color process
Two hardcover books in a slipcase

€ 135.00 / £ 125.00 / US$ 150.00
ISBN 978-3-95829-506-3

Drawn from Ed Clark's extensive personal archive of photographs, negatives, contact sheets and scrapbooks, these three volumes reveal the work of a key figure from the golden age of American photojournalism. From the pageantry of politics to the rhythms of small-town life, from movie stars to the working class, Clark covered the defining personalities and events of his age.

Ed Clark is one of the twentieth century's most fascinating and important "unknown" photographers. A gifted photojournalist, Clark began his career in 1929 with *The Tennessean* newspaper in Nashville, and went on to work for 22 years for *Life* magazine. He photographed many of *Life*'s most important assignments during the period of the magazine's greatest cultural impact; Clark's images helped shape a nation's sense of itself and the world. His vast range of subjects includes the Nuremberg war crimes trials, the conflict over civil rights in the late 1940s and early '50s, Hollywood stars and the movie industry of the '50s, the people and arts of the Soviet Union, and the White House during the Eisenhower and Kennedy administrations. Through Clark's eyes, we witness some of the central episodes and themes of the post-war world.

The days were never long enough for me while on assignment. I still love holding a camera, looking through the lens to see what I can see.
Ed Clark

Co-published with the Meserve-Kunhardt Foundation

Vol. 1: Plates and illustrated timeline

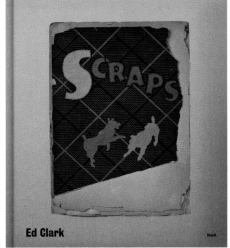

Vol. 2: Personal scrapbooks

Slipcase

Born in Memphis in 1939, William
Eggleston is regarded as one of the
greatest photographers of his generation
and a major American artist who has
fundamentally changed how the urban
landscape is viewed. He obtained his first
camera in 1957 and was later profoundly
influenced by Henri Cartier-Bresson's The
Decisive Moment. Eggleston introduced
dye-transfer printing, a previously
commercial photographic process, into the
making of artists' prints. His exhibition
"Photographs by William Eggleston" at the
Museum of Modern Art in New York in 1976
was a milestone. He was also involved in
the development of video technology in
the seventies. Eggleston is represented
in museums worldwide, and in 2008 a
retrospective of his work was held at
the Whitney Museum of American Art in
New York and at Haus der Kunst in Munich
in 2009. Eggleston's books published by
Steidl include Chromes (2011), Los Alamos
Revisited (2012), The Democratic Forest
(2015) and Election Eve (2017).

This book is a facsimile of an album of Eggleston's Polaroids assembled
by the photographer himself, and containing the only photos he made
in this medium. Consisting of 56 images taken with the Polaroid SX-70
(the now cult camera produced between 1972 and 1981) and hand-
mounted in a black leather album also produced by the company,
Polaroid SX-70 is the first publication of Eggleston's Polaroids.
The gloriously mundane subjects of these photos—a Mississippi street
sign, a telephone book, stacked crates of empty soda bottles—are
familiar Eggleston territory, but fascinatingly *all* of these Polaroids
were taken outdoors. They are rare records of Eggleston's strolls or
drives in and around Mississippi, complement the majority of his work
made with color negative film or color slides, and show his ironic flair
for photo-sequencing in book form.

*Something new always slowly changes right in front of your eyes—it
just happens.* William Eggleston

William Eggleston
Polaroid SX-70

Book design by William Eggleston, Duncan Whyte
and Gerhard Steidl
24 pages
10.4 × 10.8 in. / 26.5 × 27.5 cm
56 color photographs
Four-color process
Embossed leatherbound hardcover

€ 65.00 / £ 58.00 / US$ 75.00
ISBN 978-3-95829-503-2

David Freund has a Masters of Fine
Arts from the Visual Studies Workshop,
Rochester, and has taught at Pratt
Institute and Ramapo College of New
Jersey. His exhibitions include those
at Light Gallery in New York and George
Eastman House in Rochester, and he
has received a National Endowment for
the Arts fellowship and a CAPS grant.
Freund's work is held in the collections
of the Museum of Modern Art, New York;
the Museum of Fine Arts, Houston; the
Bibliothèque Nationale, Paris; and the
Corcoran Gallery of Art, Washington D.C.
Steidl published Freund's Gas Stop in
2016.

In 2003, as David Freund was driving to Missouri to see a 102-year-old friend, she died. Reflecting on their meeting when he was a child, he stopped in Illinois to photograph an old playground. Besides swings, teeter-totters and slides, there were cannon, war memorials, a picnic area, a cornfield, and a baseball field; evocative and telling, a site of community and play. The moment launched a two-year odyssey to find and photograph such places. Freund soon realized playgrounds were an endangered species. In cities, because of safety and liability concerns, their apparatus, familiar to many childhoods, had largely been supplanted by bright structures of multicolored plastic and enameled steel. Thus, Freund focused on small towns where tradition, inertia and budget often permitted early playgrounds to survive. These were usually unoccupied, so children rarely appear in Freund's photographs, although alluded to in footprints, worn paint, and ruts under swings. Weather, light and viewpoint contribute to suggested narratives, yet the direct preservation aspect of the project is clear. As with other species that vanish, one day they are everywhere, the next, gone.

I'm trying to find and display connective tissue that might lead to understanding about myself and the world before my camera.
David Freund

David Freund
Playground Once

Text by David Freund
Book design by David Freund and Gerhard Steidl
168 pages
11.8 × 9.1 in. / 30 × 23 cm
134 black-and-white photographs
Tritone process
Hardcover

€ 45.00 / £ 40.00 / US$ 50.00
ISBN 978-3-95829-502-5

PLAYGROUND ONCE

PHOTOGRAPHS BY DAVID FREUND

Lee Friedlander was born in 1934 in
Aberdeen, Washington. In 1948 he began to
photograph seriously and by the 1960s had
become widely recognized for his all-
encompassing portrayals of the American
social landscape—a term he coined.
Friedlander's influential work has been
the subject of many seminal exhibitions
including "New Documents" and "Mirrors
and Windows," both organized by John
Szarkowski at the Museum of Modern Art,
and more than 50 books including Self
Portrait (1970), The American Monument
(1976), Factory Valleys (1982), Sticks
and Stones (2004), America By Car (2010)
and Chain Link (2017).

In the capstone volume of his epic series "The Human Clay," Lee
Friedlander has created an ode to people who work. Drawn from
his incomparable archive are photographs of individuals laboring on
the street and on stage, as well as in the field, in factories and in
fluorescent-lit offices. Performers, salespeople and athletes alike
are observed both in action and at rest by Friedlander's uncanny
eye. Opera singers are caught mid-aria, models primp backstage,
mechanics tinker and telemarketers hustle. Spanning six decades,
this humanizing compilation features over 250 photographs, many
appearing here for the first time in print.

As he worked on the room, and as it began slowly to take a shape,
he realized that for many years, unknown to himself, he had had an
image locked somewhere within him like a shamed secret, an image
that was ostensibly of a place but which was actually of himself.
John Williams, *Stoner* (1965)

Lee Friedlander
Workers
The Human Clay

Book design by Katy Homans
200 pages
11 × 9.6 in. / 27.9 × 24.4 cm
253 black-and-white photographs
Tritone
Clothbound hardcover with a tipped-in photograph

€ 50.00 / £ 45.00 / US$ 60.00
ISBN 978-3-95829-500-1

Lee Friedlander was born in 1934 in Aberdeen, Washington. In 1948 he began to photograph seriously and by the 1960s had become widely recognized for his all-encompassing portrayals of the American social landscape—a term he coined. Friedlander's influential work has been the subject of many seminal exhibitions including "New Documents" and "Mirrors and Windows," both organized by John Szarkowski at the Museum of Modern Art, and more than 50 books including Self Portrait (1970), The American Monument (1976), Factory Valleys (1982), Sticks and Stones (2004), America By Car (2010) and Chain Link (2017).

In this compendium Lee Friedlander examines the ordinary pickup truck, a quintessentially American mode of transportation. Unadorned in form as well as function, pickups have long been the vehicle of choice for farmers and tradespeople. Their well-worn beds—usually open to the elements, laid bare for all to see—have held and hauled all manner of things, from spare tires and jumbles of wires to animals and the occasional person. Friedlander, in his witty and encompassing clear-eyed idiom, has observed this most utilitarian and unapologetically personal object in its native setting: the cacophonous bricolage that is American social landscape.

Living for an hour or more inside his superb way of seeing is like taking a walk down a busy city street on a bright day: your ordinary vision is transformed into something sharper, more uncanny, more intelligent and more generous. Teju Cole, the *New York Times Magazine*

Lee Friedlander
Pickup

Book design by Katy Homans
88 pages
11.5 × 12.2 in. / 29.3 × 31 cm
78 black-and-white photographs
Tritone
Clothbound hardcover with a tipped-in photograph

€ 45.00 / £ 40.00 / US$ 50.00
ISBN 978-3-95829-501-8

Born in Chicago in 1933, Bruce Davidson began photographing at the age of ten in Oak Park, Illinois. Davidson studied at the Rochester Institute of Technology and Yale University before being drafted into the army. After leaving military service in 1957, he freelanced for Life and in 1958 became a member of Magnum Photos. Davidson's solo exhibitions include those at the Museum of Modern Art, the Smithsonian American Art Museum and the Walker Art Center, and his awards include a Guggenheim Fellowship and the first National Endowment for the Arts Grant in Photography. In 2011 he was awarded an honorary doctorate in Fine Arts from the Corcoran College of Art and Design. Davidson's books at Steidl include Outside Inside (2010), Subway (2011), Black & White (2012) and England / Scotland 1960 (2014).

Lesser Known presents Bruce Davidson's photos made between 1955 and 1993 that have been overshadowed until now. Consisting of 130 images that have been consistently overlooked throughout Davidson's long career, the book is the result of a year-long undertaking by the photographer and his studio to examine 60 years of contact sheets and edit individual images into a singular work that plots his professional and personal growth. *Lesser Known* showcases Davidson's perpetual versatility and adaptability as a photographer through a focus on early assignments, the intimate documentation of his family life and smaller series such as unpublished color photographs from major bodies of work including "East 100th Street" and "Campers."

This new body of work reflects both a passion and purpose over time.
Bruce Davidson

Bruce Davidson
Lesser Known

Edited by Teresa Kroemer, Meagan Connolly and Bruce Davidson
Foreword by Bruce Davidson
Book design by Duncan Whyte / Steidl Design
192 pages
11.4 × 11.4 in. / 29 × 29 cm
114 black-and-white and 16 color photographs
Tritone and four-colour process
Clothbound hardcover with dust jacket

€ 58.00 / £ 55.00 / US$ 60.00
ISBN 978-3-95829-321-2

Frank Gohlke was born in Wichita Falls, Texas, in 1942. In 1967 he abandoned the study of literature to become a photographer, encouraged in his decision by Walker Evans, who saw his first photographs, and Paul Caponigro, with whom he studied informally at his home in Connecticut. Gohlke has received two fellowships from the Guggenheim Foundation, two from the National Endowment for the Arts, and a Fulbright Research Fellowship to Kazakhstan in 2013-14. His work has been exhibited and collected internationally, including three solo shows at the Museum of Modern Art. Gohlke's books include Mount St. Helens (2005), Accommodating Nature (2007), Thoughts on Landscape (2009) and Landscape as Longing with Joel Sternfeld and Suketu Mehta published by Steidl in 2016.

Frank Gohlke
Measure of Emptiness

Text by Frank Gohlke
Book design by Frank Gohlke and Gerhard Steidl
120 pages
8.8 × 11.2 in. / 22.4 × 28.4 cm
45 black-and-white photographs
Tritone
Clothbound hardcover with a tipped-in photograph

€ 48.00 / £ 45.00 / US$ 55.00
ISBN 978-3-95829-498-1

Measure of Emptiness is a meditation on the vast spaces of the Great Plains, the heartland of American agricultural productivity, and the centrality of the grain elevator to its social, cultural and symbolic life. In photographs made between 1972 and 1977 with the support of fellowships from the Guggenheim Foundation and the National Endowment of Art, Frank Gohlke traveled back and forth through the central tier of states from his home in Minneapolis, Minnesota, to the Texas Panhandle, seeking an answer to the puzzle of the grain elevators' extraordinary power as architecture in a landscape whose primary dramas were in the sky.

"In the United States there is more space where nobody is than where anybody is," said Gertrude Stein. The Great Plains are characterized by this spaciousness, and by the presence of windowless, rumbling, enormous grain elevators, rising above the steeples of churches to announce the presence of the town and to explain, in great measure, the lives and livelihoods of its inhabitants. Why did their builders choose that particular form to fulfill and practical necessity? And does the experience of great emptiness shape what people think, feel and do?

We are powerful, we build for the centuries, our monuments rival those of other heroic ages; we are insignificant, our hold on this landscape is tenuous, nature and time erode our greatest creations as if they were dust. What lingers in the memory, though, is the image of a solitary, upright form in the middle distance of an endless plain.
Frank Gohlke

Frank Gohlke was born in 1942 in Wichita Falls, Texas. In 1967 he abandoned the study of literature to become a photographer, encouraged by Walker Evans, who saw his first photographs, and Paul Caponigro, with whom he studied informally at his home in Connecticut. Gohlke has received two fellowships from the Guggenheim Foundation, two from the National Endowment for the Arts, and a Fulbright Research Fellowship to Kazakhstan in 2013-14. His work has been exhibited and collected internationally, including three solo shows at the Museum of Modern Art. His books include Measure of Emptiness (1992), Mount St. Helens (2005), Accommodating Nature (2007), Thoughts on Landscape (2009), and Landscapes as Longing with Joel Sternfeld and Suketu Mehta, published by Steidl in 2016.

In the summer of 1971 Frank Gohlke moved with his wife and young daughter from Middlebury, Vermont to Minneapolis, Minnesota. His vocation as a photographer had begun four years prior, but he had yet to define the subject that would occupy him for the next 45 years: the landscapes of ordinary life.

The three bodies of work brought together in *Speeding Trucks and Other Follies* were all made between Gohlke's arrival in Minneapolis and the end of 1972 when he began photographing grain elevators, a project that first established his renown. In different ways these early series obliquely describe Gohlke's process of adjustment to his new surroundings.

The "Speeding Trucks" photos of the first section began when Gohlke noticed how the shadows of the elm trees that once lined most Minneapolis streets were momentarily materialized on the bodies of passing trucks. The travel trailers in the second section were all found in a Minnesota State Park on one of the family's infrequent camping trips, while late-night rambles through Gohlke's Minneapolis neighborhood led organically to his series of dramatic night pictures in the last section. Notwithstanding their various subject matter, Gohlke's photos in this book collectively perform a kind of timeless alchemy on the everyday stuff of visual experience.

Looking at these photos, it's hard not to believe that things really look like that; but we know they don't. In the interstice between the picture's testimony and the evidence of our senses is where my photos reside. Frank Gohlke

Frank Gohlke
Speeding Trucks and Other Follies

Book design by Frank Gohlke and Holger Feroudj
96 pages
9.6 × 10.2 in. / 24.5 × 26 cm
48 black-and-white photographs
Tritone
Clothbound hardcover with a tipped-in photograph

€ 44.00 / £ 40.00 / US$ 50.00
ISBN 978-3-95829-254-3

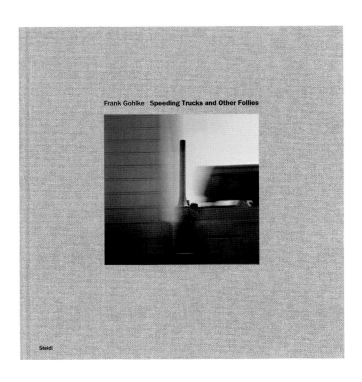

Born in New Jersey, Henry Wessel
(1942-2018) was awarded two Guggenheim
fellowships and three fellowships from
the National Endowment for the Arts. His
work is held in the permanent collections
of major American, European and Asian
museums, and his solo exhibitions include
those at the Museum of Modern Art in New
York and the Museum of Contemporary Art
in Los Angeles. Steidl has published many
of Wessel's books, including Waikiki
(2011) Incidents (2013) and Traffic /
Sunset Park / Continental Divide (2016).

In the fall of 1960 Henry Wessel left his family home in New Jersey
to attend college in Central Pennsylvania. At the time, he had never
been further west than Philadelphia. On Friday afternoons, to offset
the daily classroom cadence, Wessel would pack a knapsack and
hitchhike west. Once Saturday afternoon had ended, he would cross
the highway and hitchhike back east, hoping to arrive in time for class
on Monday morning. Though Wessel would not begin to photograph
until years later, these early forays west planted seeds of discovery
that proved fruitful for decades to come.

Hitchhike is a westward journey from the grassy farmlands in
the Midwest to the wide, open, dusty landscape further west. The
sequence of photos draws from Wessel's 50-year archive and includes
images of barns, gas stations, traveling salesmen, dogs asleep in truck
beds, families eating in diners and open highways—all lit by bright
western light, almost physical in its presence.

*The process of photographing is a pleasure: eyes open, receptive,
sensing, and at some point, connecting. It's thrilling to be outside
your mind, your eyes far ahead of your thoughts.* Henry Wessel

Henry Wessel
Hitchhike

Book design by Steidl Design
80 pages
11.7 x 11.4 in. / 29.7 x 29 cm
36 black-and-white photographs
Tritone
Clothbound hardcover with a tipped-in photograph

€ 55.00 / £ 50.00 / US$ 65.00
ISBN 978-3-95829-569-8

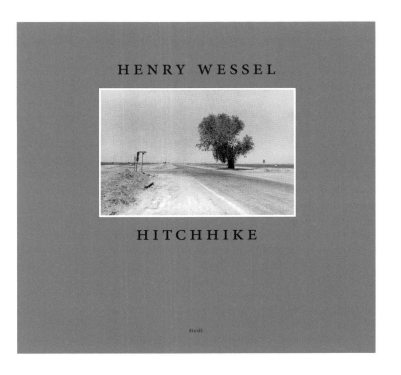

Walkabout

Man Alone

Botanical Census

Born in New Jersey, Henry Wessel (1942-2018) was awarded two Guggenheim fellowships and three fellowships from the National Endowment for the Arts. His work is held in the permanent collections of major American, European and Asian museums, and his solo exhibitions include those at the Museum of Modern Art in New York and the Museum of Contemporary Art in Los Angeles. Steidl has published many of Wessel's books, including Waikiki (2011) Incidents (2013) and Traffic / Sunset Park / Continental Divide (2016).

This book presents three independent bodies of work by Henry Wessel from the past five decades. Each is a precise sequence recreating the experience of passing through the territory described. "Walkabout" invites the viewer to walk with Wessel through working-class neighborhoods and bordering urban areas. The photos show sun-soaked homes, cars, bars, alleyways, gas stations and cyclone fences, reminding us that intuition can lead to dramatic possibilities anywhere. Wessel describes his approach: "At the core of this receptivity is a process that might be called soft eyes. It is a physical sensation. You are not looking for something. You are open, receptive. At some point, you are in front of something that you cannot ignore." "Man Alone" comprises photographs Wessel made of men in San Francisco. What at first seems a study of the gesture and gait of the urban man is actually a collection of individuals: each man's singularity is described through the interrelatedness of stride, garb, facial expression and the shape of the photo. Wessel's final series "Botanical Census" meanders through city streets, parks, roadsides and open fields. Images of bushes, succulents, trees, topiary and weeds, rendered by sharp-edged light, reveal the aesthetic possibilities growing all around us.

Arranging a precise sequence of photographs is similar to arranging words to create a poem. The meaning comes from what is being described and the shape of the description. Henry Wessel

Henry Wessel
Walkabout / Man Alone / Botanical Census

Book design by Steidl Design
184 pages
11.7 x 11.4 in. / 29.7 x 29 cm
84 black-and-white photographs
Tritone
Clothbound hardcover with three tipped-in photographs

€ 65.00 / £ 60.00 / US$ 75.00
ISBN 978-3-95829-570-4

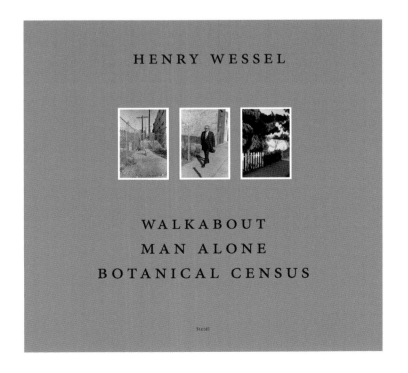

The images of Mary Ellen Mark (1940-2015) are icons of documentary photography. Her 20 books include Ward 81 (1979), Falkland Road (1981) and Indian Circus (1993). Her last book Tiny: Streetwise Revisited (2015) is a culmination of 32 years documenting Erin Blackwell (Tiny), who was featured in Martin Bell's 1985 film Streetwise and Mark's 1988 book of the same name. Mark's humanistic work has been exhibited and published in magazines worldwide.

Mary Ellen Mark
Book of Everything

Edited by Martin Bell
Texts by Mary Ellen Mark, Martin Bell and others
Book design by Atelier Dyakova
704 pages
9.6 × 12.7 in. / 24.5 × 32.2 cm
510 black-and-white and 90 color photographs
Tritone
Clothbound hardcover in a slipcase

€ 125.00 / £ 120.00 / US$ 150.00
ISBN 978-3-95829-565-0

Conceived and edited by film director Martin Bell, Mary Ellen Mark's husband and collaborator for 30 years, the *Book of Everything* celebrates in over 600 images and diverse texts Mark's extraordinary life, work and vision. From 1963 to her death in 2015, Mark told brilliant, intimate, provocative stories of characters whom she met and engaged with—often in perpetuity. There was nothing casual or unprepared about Mark's approach; she unfailingly empathized with the people and places she photographed.

For this comprehensive book Bell has selected images from Mark's thousands of contact-sheets and chromes—from over two million frames in total. These include her own now iconic choices, those published once and since lost in time, as well as some of her as yet unpublished preferences. Bell complements these with a few selections of his own. Along with Mark's pictures made in compelling, often tragic circumstances, the *Book of Everything* includes recollections from friends, colleagues and many of those she photographed. Mark's own thoughts reveal doubts and insecurities, her ideas about the individuals and topics she depicted, as well as the challenges of the business of photography.

I became a photographer because photography found me. Once I started to take pictures there was no choice. That was just what I was and what I wanted to do and what I wanted to be. Mary Ellen Mark

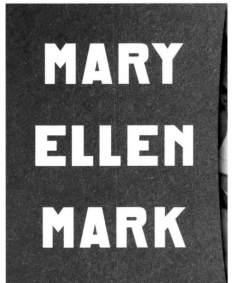
Slipcase front

Slipcase back

Book

John Cohen, born in 1932 in New York, is a photographer, filmmaker and founding member of the New Lost City Ramblers. A masters graduate of Yale University, Cohen participated in the artistic circles of late 1950s and early '60s New York, and photographed Robert Frank's film Pull My Daisy (1959). He has made numerous books and films, and produced recordings of traditional American musicians including Dillard Chandler and Roscoe Holcomb. The Library of Congress has acquired his archive. Cohen's books with Steidl include Past Present Peru (2010), The High and Lonesome Sound (2012) and Cheap rents … and de Kooning (2016).

In the summer of 1955 a relatively naive and uninformed John Cohen crossed the straits of Gibraltar. He arrived in Tangier with a handwritten note in cursive Arabic; the man who had composed it in New York had told him to "keep this paper far from your passport." Cohen had no idea why or indeed what the note said; it was not addressed to a specific person. He was simply instructed to look for a certain man when he arrived, who would then send him to "the others." Cohen's otherwise straightforward trip to make photographs in Morocco thus began with a sense of intrigue and perhaps risk.

This was Cohen's first journey outside America to see the world. In his words: "The camera led my way to a distant culture, along with the desire to represent what I could see and sense there, and not be distracted by chronology or thought. My photographs were intended to be a sensual response to light and to the people who inhabited these spaces. These Morocco photos were … an indication of what was to come."

By the time I got to Rabat the sense of tension was unmistakable. There were French soldiers marching through the streets, there was the rumor that on the Sultan's day, August 20, there would be uprisings. And that the exiled Sultan was not in Madagascar, but was on the moon. John Cohen

John Cohen
Morocco
Look up to the moon

Text by John Cohen
Book design by Steidl Design
180 pages
8.9 x 9.1 in. / 22.5 x 23 cm
90 black-and-white and 10 color photographs
Tritone and four-color process
Clothbound hardcover

€ 45.00 / £ 40.00 / US$ 50.00
ISBN 978-3-95829-555-1

Born in San Francisco in 1955, Jeff Brouws is a self-taught photographer. His work is held in important collections including the Whitney Museum of American Art, the Fogg Art Museum at Harvard University and the Princeton University Art Museum. Brouws is the author of seven books including Twentysix Abandoned Gasoline Stations (1992) and Approaching Nowhere (2006).

Jeff Brouws
Silent Monoliths
The Coaling Tower Project

Texts by Marcella Hackbardt and John P. Hankey
Book design by Jeff Brouws
208 pages
11 x 11 in. / 27.9 x 27.9 cm
158 black-and-white photographs
Tritone
Clothbound hardcover with dust jacket

€ 65.00 / £ 60.00 / US$ 75.00
ISBN 978-3-95829-554-4

Jeff Brouws has spent the last 30 years photographing various aspects of the American cultural landscape, often assembling typologies of common architectural forms in everyday environments. In *Silent Monoliths* he documents a variety of concrete coaling towers standing dormant in isolated brownfields or along active railroad lines. Built between 1907 and '56 these remnants of railroading's past were once used to dispense coal into steam locomotives. Seemingly impervious to the vicissitudes of time, decay or outright removal, these sculptural examples of former industrial brawn recall an earlier technological era most of us never witnessed. Because of this we glimpse—in real time—what Walker Evans once termed the "historical contemporary" of the modern world.

Brouws practices an evidentiary form of photography, taking stand-alone portraits of coaling towers in homage to Hilla and Bernd Becher, as well as wider views revealing their broader contexts and landscapes. These two approaches reflect his dual interests in the New Topographics from the 1970s, as well as the compiling of typologies—a style of image making with historic roots traceable to the invention of photography itself as seen by Louis Daguerre's photo of his fossil collection and William Henry Fox Talbot's botanical photograms. Brouws' coaling towers emerge in dialogue with these nineteenth- and twentieth-century predecessors.

In Brouws' exceptional artistic and documentary project, he discovers beautifully unexpected architectures. They rise with vitality over present and absent railways, locating a landscape of transformation.
Marcella Hackbardt

Born in 1944, Anders Petersen studied
photography at Fotoskolan and later at the
Institute for Cinema, Radio, Television
and Theatre, both in Stockholm. In 1970
he founded the group of photographers
Saftra together with Kenneth Gustavsson.
Petersen is perhaps best known for
his photos of the colorful, often
unconventional, patrons of Café Lehmitz
in Hamburg's St. Pauli, resulting in his
seminal book Café Lehmitz (1978). He has
published and exhibited his photography
extensively and in 2014 was the subject
of a retrospective at the Bibliothéque
National de France in Paris.

Zoo is a wild ride through Anders Petersen's oeuvre, a racy edit of his
work that has animals as its central theme. Whether they be conscious
portraits of animals or a haphazard photographic encounter with a
woman's legs in python-print tights, Petersen draws out the animal
and animalistic in all that he sees. At a typical zoo we are the specta-
tors, peering in on creatures as they go about their existence, mostly
oblivious to our presence. Yet in *Zoo* we find ourselves both behind
and before the bars of the cage—with Petersen as the delighted
zookeeper.

Shoot from the gut, edit with the brain. Anders Petersen

Anders Petersen
Zoo

Edited and book design by Greger Ulf Nilson
320 pages
8.3 x 11 in. / 21 x 28 cm
240 black-and-white photographs
Tritone
Half-linen hardcover

€ 65.00 / £ 60.00 / US$ 75.00
ISBN 978-3-95829-333-5

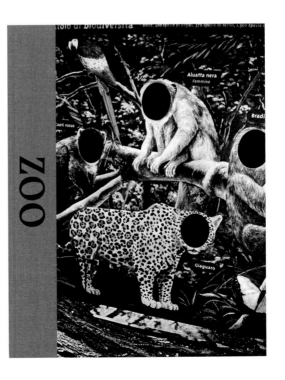

Born in 1944, Anders Petersen studied photography at Fotoskolan and later at the Institute for Cinema, Radio, Television and Theatre, both in Stockholm. In 1970 he founded the group of photographers Saftra together with Kenneth Gustavsson. Petersen is perhaps best known for his photos of the colorful, often unconventional, patrons of Café Lehmitz in Hamburg's St. Pauli, resulting in his seminal book Café Lehmitz (1978). He has published and exhibited his photography extensively and in 2014 was the subject of a retrospective at the Bibliothéque National de France in Paris.

This book is the latest of Anders Petersen's award-winning *City Diaries*, the first three of which are now out of print. Throughout his career Petersen has traveled extensively and documented life beyond the margins of polite society, a shadowy world of pleasure and sin including prostitutes, transvestites, alcoholics, nighttime lovers and adult conflict. Through his candid, empathetic yet somewhat detached eye, he discloses difficult realities such as drug addiction with a sense of bewilderment and currency. *City Diary #4* shows Petersen's ongoing photographic engagement with the gritty and beautiful in life as it unfolds before him.

I'm a kind of diary photographer. I try not to take pictures as I see them, but as I feel them. I'm interested in imperfection.
Anders Petersen

Anders Petersen
City Diary #4

Edited and book design by Greger Ulf Nilson
64 pages
9.2 x 12.2 in. / 23.4 x 31 cm
56 black-and-white photographs
Tritone
Half-linen softcover in an envelope

€ 40.00 / £ 35.00 / US$ 50.00
ISBN 978-3-95829-334-2

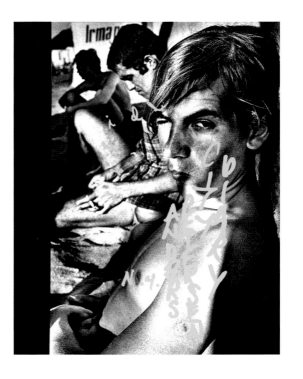

Born in 1933 in Visby on the island of Gotland, Gunnar Smoliansky is a major Swedish photographer. He has devoted himself to the medium since the 1950s, originally working as a photographer's assistant and attending courses under Christer Strömholm. Between 1956 and 1963 he worked as an industrial photographer and since the 1970s has practiced as an independent artist. Smoliansky photographs exclusively in black and white and develops by hand in the darkroom. Stockholm has been the focus of Smoliansky's photographic world, particularly the areas of Södermalm and Saltsjö-Boo where he has lived and worked for most of his life. Steidl published Smoliansky's One Picture at a Time in 2009.

Promenade Pictures collects a suite of humble yet profound pictures taken by Gunnar Smoliansky in the 1970s and '80s during long walks throughout Stockholm and its surrounds. The figure of the *flâneur* in literature and art history is often a self-indulgent one, but Smoliansky rejects any hint of decadence. His sole concern is to discover the modest abstractions of the everyday: the fluid lines of a gnarled tree trunk; the graphic shapes of streets, shadows, stairs and tiles; the delicate landscape of crumpled bed sheets. Smoliansky's vision is as patient as it is single-minded: he stubbornly draws out and refines the geometric beauty of objects we would otherwise miss.

Smoliansky created these photos, as all of his work, with an analogue camera and developed the prints in his own darkroom. In these pictures he lays particular emphasis on the painterly tonalities of the prints, from warm sepia to cool black and white, in order to recreate variations of daylight. This new Steidl edition of *Promenade Pictures* is an expanded version of a smaller book, originally published by Moderna Museet in Stockholm in 1986.

Gunnar Smoliansky's sober photographs are free of grand gestures. There is always a kind of invisible umbilical cord between his pictures and reality. Smoliansky never cuts it. He continues to take pictures with the unaffected conviction of someone who knows exactly what he is doing. Joanna Persman

Gunnar Smoliansky
Promenade Pictures

Edited by Greger Ulf Nilson
Text by Joanna Persman
Book design by Greger Ulf Nilson
128 pages
6.1 x 9.4 in. / 15.5 x 24 cm
74 black-and-white images
Tritone
Softcover

€ 45.00 / £ 40.00 / US$ 50.00
ISBN 978-3-95829-332-8

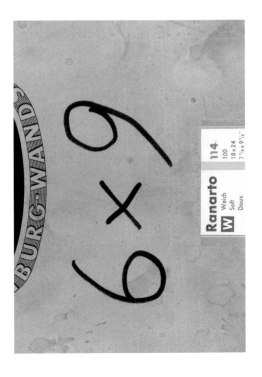

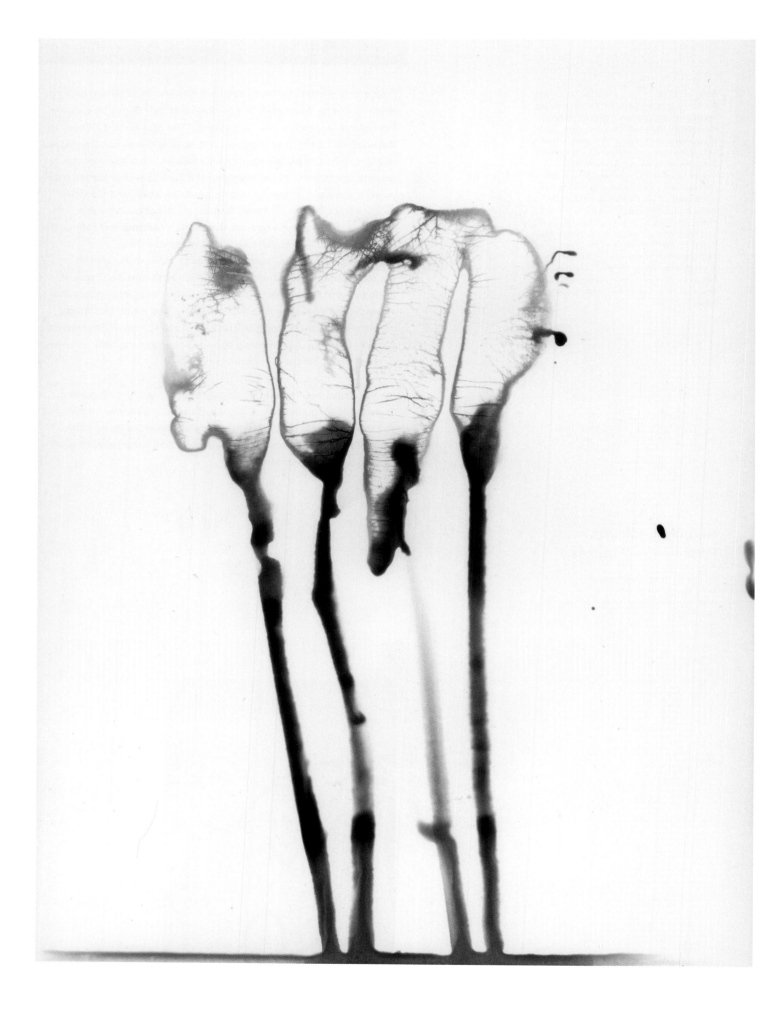

Born in 1933 in Visby on the island of Gotland, Gunnar Smoliansky is a major Swedish photographer. He has devoted himself to the medium since the 1950s, originally working as a photographer's assistant and attending courses under Christer Strömholm. Between 1956 and 1963 he worked as an industrial photographer and since the 1970s has practiced as an independent artist. Smoliansky photographs exclusively in black and white and develops by hand in the darkroom. Stockholm has been the focus of Smoliansky's photographic world, particularly the areas of Södermalm and Saltsjö-Boo where he has lived and worked for most of his life. Steidl published Smoliansky's One Picture at a Time in 2009.

This book contains more than 400 pictures of Gunnar Smoliansky's hands, each a spontaneous composition crafted by the photographer in his traditional darkroom. The inspiration for this series was unexpected and Smoliansky pursued it with an artist's rigor, creating a complex series, each image a nuanced variation on a theme. Some pictures are deceptively simple, hardly recognizable abstractions; others are realistic, revealing even the texture of Smoliansky's palm; while others still are almost violent inky overlappings. By bypassing the tool of the camera and reinterpreting the photogram, Smoliansky revisits one of the earliest means of photographic picture making and creates a gestural space between photography and drawing.

I don't know what it was that made me start on these pictures.
Always after the end of the working day. A tired developer, new fix.
A sheet of glass in the wet bench to splash on.
Expired 18 × 24 papers with different surfaces and tones.
What I did was to open a box in darkroom lighting and take out some papers between my thumb and my index finger.
Then the work continued in ordinary room lighting.
I numbered the papers, all of which are presented here in the book.
Gunnar Smoliansky

Gunnar Smoliansky
Hands

Edited by Greger Ulf Nilson
Text by Gunnar Smoliansky
Book design by Greger Ulf Nilson
440 pages
8.7 x 10.9 in. / 22.2 x 27.7 cm
401 black-and-white images
Tritone
Clothbound hardcover

€ 65.00 / £ 60.00 / US$ 75.00
ISBN 978-3-95829-331-1

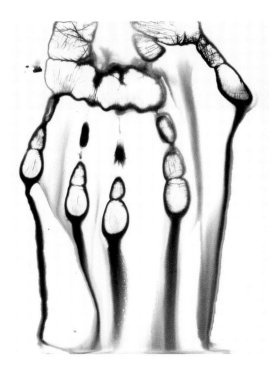

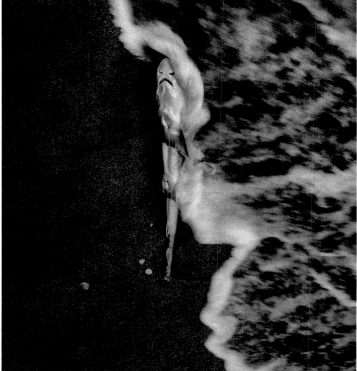

Christer Strömholm (1918-2002) was one
of the most influential Scandinavian
photographers and the recipient of the
1997 Hasselblad Award. Born in Stockholm,
in 1946 Strömholm moved to Paris where
he discovered photography. Between 1949
and '54 he joined the German group of
photographers Fotoforum, led by Otto
Steinert, and participated in their
exhibitions in Europe and America. Perhaps
Strömholm's most influential series
is "Les Amies de la Place Blanche,"
documenting the transsexuals of Paris'
Place Blanche in the late fifties and
early sixties. From 1962 to '74 he was
director of Fotoskolan in Stockholm where
he trained over 1,200 students, many of
whom would become leading photographers
including Anders Petersen, Dawid, Bille
August and Gunnar Smoliansky.

This book presents little-known photos by the legendary Christer Strömholm selected by Gunnar Smoliansky. In the late eighties gallerist Kim Klein proposed a small exhibition of Strömholm's pictures at the Lido Gallery in Stockholm. Strömholm agreed and entrusted Smoliansky with making a selection from his early 6 x 6 Rolleiflex negatives. Smoliansky was delighted to do so—the planned ten to twelve photos soon ballooned to 70—and he printed two sets, one for Strömholm and one for himself. The photos date from the late 1940s and early '50s and show Strömholm's formative years in Paris, the south of France, Morocco and other destinations. Most of these pictures had never before been printed, let alone publicized, until that exhibition of 1990.

When I think about it, and when I look closely at my pictures, they are all, in their own way, nothing but self-portraits—a part of my life.
Christer Strömholm

Christer Strömholm
Lido

Edited by Gunnar Smoliansky and Greger Ulf Nilson
Text by Gunnar Smoliansky
Book design by Greger Ulf Nilson
96 pages
11.8 × 11.8 in. / 29.7 × 29.7 cm
42 black-and-white photographs
Tritone
Clothbound hardcover with a tipped-in photograph

€ 45.00 / £ 40.00 / US$ 50.00
ISBN 978-3-95829-335-9

CHRISTER STRÖMHOLM   LIDO

Ed Kashi is a photojournalist, filmmaker, speaker and educator. A member of VII Photo Agency, Kashi is recognized for his complex imagery and compelling rendering of the human condition. Along with numerous awards, including Pictures of the Year International Multimedia Photographer of the Year 2015, Kashi's photos have been published and exhibited worldwide, and have generated eight books, including Sugar Cane / Syrian Refugees published by Steidl in 2016.

If Cartier-Bresson's "decisive moment" reflects a situation perfectly in tune with the photographer's intuition, flawlessly combining the elements of composition and timing, then Ed Kashi's "abandoned moment" is the result of an imprecise instant of surrender. The photos in this book are moving glimpses of transitory events filled with an untamed, frenetic energy—the perfect chaos of everyday life.

For nearly 40 years, Kashi has photographed the instantaneous imperfections that define his abandoned moment. Seeking to reconcile the dichotomy that many people like to look at photos but do not want to be photographed, Kashi stumbled upon a method of uncontrolled photographic observation while still a young practioner. In contrast to his journalistic approach of personally connecting with his subject, keenly observing visual elements and going in-depth, in *Abandoned Moments* Kashi employs geometry, mood and emotion to capture spontaneous experiences with a touch of the mysterious and sometimes fictional.

Ed Kashi is intelligent, brave and compassionate. He always under-stands the nuances of his subjects. He fearlessly goes where few would venture. And he sympathetically captures the soul of each situation. Ed is one of the best of a new breed of photojournalistic artists.
David Griffin, former director of photography at *National Geographic*

Ed Kashi
Abandoned Moments

Edited by Jennifer Larsen, Marjorie Steffe and Mallika Vora
Foreword by Alison Nordstrom
Book design by Mallika Vora
128 pages
11 × 8.5 in. / 27.9 × 21.6 cm
26 black-and-white and 42 color photographs
Four-color process
Clothbound hardcover

€ 40.00 / £ 35.00 / US$ 45.00
ISBN 978-3-95829-274-1

Born in 1981 and 1987 in the Parisian
suburbs, Yves Marchand and Romain Meffre
started photographing independently in
2001. In 2005 they began to collaborate
on The Ruins of Detroit, which Steidl
published to acclaim in 2010 and which
is now in its fourth edition. Steidl has
also published Marchand and Meffre's
Gunkanjima (2013).

Between 2014 and 2016, Yves Marchand and Romain Meffre visited
400 of the more than 4,000 internal courtyards in Budapest. Their
large number and variety of styles incorporating different facets of
classicism and modernity make them a remarkable architectural
phenomenon—a charming second city within the city.

Marchand and Meffre systematically documented these courtyards, producing a typological series that describes this particular
form of collective housing and reflects the city's tumultuous history,
its changing political regimes and economy. *Budapest Courtyards*
allows us to delight in the crumbling grandeur of the courtyards, and
observe the developments and personal strategies of adaptation
which they evidence.

*In line with their work on Detroit and Gunkanjima Island, Marchand
and Meffre have managed to navigate two extremes at the intimate
heart of the Hungarian capital to best superimpose the Budapests of
today and the last century, producing an extensive series that offers
an untarnished view of this unique heritage.* Hélène Bienvenu

Yves Marchand and Romain Meffre
Budapest Courtyards

Text by Hélène Bienvenu
Book design by Yves Marchand and Romain Meffre
180 pages
10.2 × 13 in. / 26 × 33 cm
168 color photographs
Four-color process
Clothbound hardcover

€ 68.00 / £ 65.00 / US$ 75.00
ISBN 978-3-95829-255-0

Ken Light is a social documentary photographer with a particular focus on America. His nine books include To The Promised Land (1988), Texas Death Row (1997) and Valley of Shadows and Dreams (2012). Light has exhibited internationally, including solo shows at the International Center of Photography in New York, the Oakland Museum of California and the Visual Studies Workshop in Rochester. Among his awards are two National Endowment for the Arts fellowships and the Dorothea Lange Fellowship. Light is the Reva and David Logan Professor of Photojournalism at the University of California, Berkeley.

This book of Ken Light's earliest photos from 1969 to 1974 documents the social, cultural and political landscapes of America as they roiled with upheaval, and marks his transformation from a student activist to a concerned social documentary photographer. Light's frontline photos show people across race, class and political lines, and counteract the truncated memory of the sixties that has often been promoted by the media.

Light's journey through America begins with teenagers at the beach with their transistor radio. Here is the quiet before the storm: high-school students with their Eisenhower textbook, retirees playing cards and cafeteria workers quietly striking. And then, suddenly, the new, alternative worldview bursts forth: the Vietnam Moratorium, the Republican Convention, riots, POWs returning home, Nixon's resignation. *What's Going On?* reveals how politically divided the United States was as a progressive, more egalitarian world order was foisted upon it. It stirs long forgotten memories for those who were present, creates a cultural and historical legacy for the youth of today, and argues that much of our current turmoil is the result of cataclysmic changes of the sixties we have not yet absorbed.

Light shows us the collective movement forward, in love and in struggle, on both sides of the political divide, and exemplifies the power of photography to both reveal and form those movements.
Martha Rosler, *Aperture*

Ken Light
What's Going On? 1969–1974

Edited by Melanie Light
Text by Ken Light
Book design by Bonnie Briant Design
192 pages
11.7 × 13 in. / 29.7 × 33 cm
139 black-and-white photographs
Tritone
Clothbound hardcover

€ 58.00 / £ 55.00 / US$ 65.00
ISBN 978-3-95829-396-0

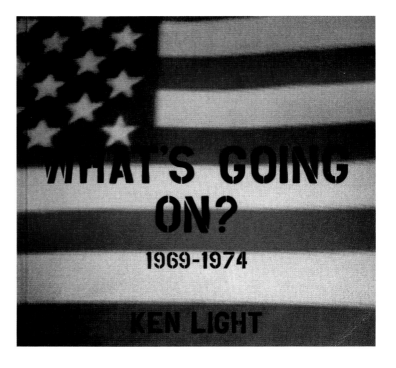

Born in Kentucky in 1950, Shelby Lee Adams attended the Cleveland Institute of Art where he was exposed to the photographs of the Farm Security Administration; these inspired him to take photos of the people of Appalachia, an ongoing project that has shaped his life's work. Adams' awards include a survey grant and fellowship from the National Endowment for the Arts (1978, 1992), grants from the Polaroid Corporation (1989-92), and the John Simon Guggenheim Photography Fellowship (2010). His work is held in collections including the Museum of Modern Art, New York, and Musée de l'Elysée, Lausanne, Switzerland. Adams exhibits and teaches internationally, and is curently developing his archive with the Center of Creative Photography in Tucson, Arizona.

The Book of Life presents Shelby Lee Adam's color photographs of four generations of the Appalachian people. Adams began photographing the inhabitations of the rural Appalachian mountain range in 1974, using black-and-white film and Polaroid materials. In time he also worked with color Kodachrome film, invariably returning to the Eastern Kentucky region where he was born. By 2010 Adams was photographing exclusively in digital color, and this book marks the first time he is sharing his color work.

Adams has consistently focused on the valleys and homes of Kentucky families, relatives and neighbors in a predominantly seven-county region. He has often revisited individuals and families many times over decades, distributing his photos and books while creating new pictures. This personal approach has led to the creation of genuine and deep relationships between photographer and subject, in which the subject is often involved in unusually creative ways, verbalizing the emotions they would like to express during the shoot, and where and how they would like to be depicted.

These portraits are, in a way, self-portraits that represent a long autobiographical exploration of creativity, imagination, vision, repulsion and salvation. My greatest fear as a photographer is to l ook into the eyes of my subject and not see my own reflection.
Shelby Lee Adams

Shelby Lee Adams
The Book of Life

Texts by Shelby Lee Adams and John Rohrbach
Book design by Shelby Lee Adams and Gerhard Steidl
184 pages
9.4 x 12.6 in. / 24 x 32 cm
85 color photographs
Four-color process
Clothbound hardcover

€ 50.00 / £ 45.00 / US$ 55.00
ISBN 978-3-95829-418-9

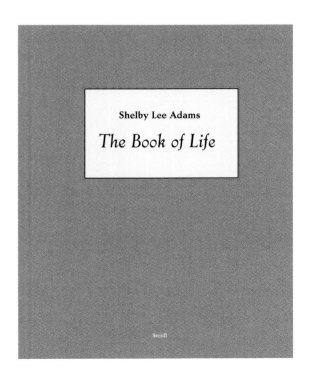

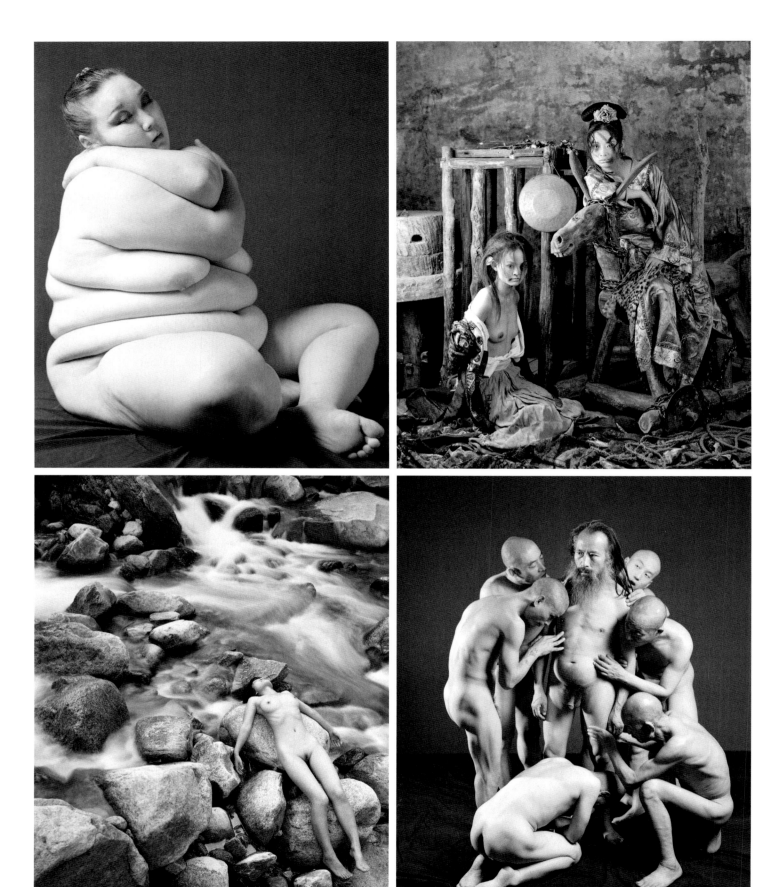

Liu Zheng was born in Wuqiang Province,
China in 1969 and grew up in a mining
district of Shanxi Province. He studied
in the Engineering and Optics Department
of the Beijing Institute of Technology,
and in 1995 co-founded the journal New
Photography. Between 1994 and 2001 Liu
Zheng traveled extensively throughout
China to produce his series "The Chinese."
Outside China his work has been shown in
France, Italy and New York.

Liu Zheng
Dream Shock

Edited by Mark Holborn
Introduction by Mark Holborn
Book design by Jesse Holborn
108 pages
11.5 × 12.1 in. / 29.2 × 30.8 cm
60 black-and-white photographs
Tritone
Clothbound hardcover with a tipped-in photograph

€ 40.00 / £ 35.00 / US$ 45.00
ISBN 978-3-95829-267-3

The "dream shock" of Liu Zheng's title refers to an awakening as if from a deep sleep. There is a moment between sleep and consciousness in which the dream state and conscious reality collide. It is a fertile, erotic and sometimes violent area of the mind, in which both exquisite and tortured imagery may surface.

Liu Zheng is one of the few Chinese photographers whose work has reached the West. The exhibition of his extensive series "The Chinese" at ICP in New York in 2004 and the accompanying Steidl book indicated he was working on the borders between the documentary tradition and the extended portrait school of August Sander. His background with the *Workers' Daily* suggests his grounding as a photojournalist. Yet Liu Zheng's vision does not echo the common view of China, characterized by anonymity in the sheer mass of the population or by the momentum of industry. Frequently the subjects of his portraits are those on the fringes of Chinese society; his outsiders contribute to an unfamiliar collective portrait of a nation.

Dream Shock brings us to another space that exists in the mind itself. Some of the characters, such as a beautiful Peking Opera singer, may be half-familiar, but the historical references to a brutal occupation and the sexual explicitness take us into unprecedented territory. Elaborate scenes are delicately choreographed in a series of terrifying tableaux. The directness of photographic evidence exists alongside studio staging that is pure and unsettling theatre. We enter a wholly new domain.

Liu Zheng has eclipsed all the previous photographic clichés of the Chinese people and Chinese culture. Liu's photography is like a window opening onto a grand view of the cruelty and the darkness of this culture. Gu Zheng

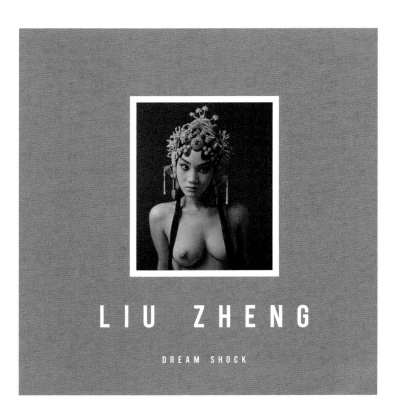

LIU ZHENG

DREAM SHOCK

Ernst Haas was born in Vienna in 1921
and took up photography after World
War II. His early work on returning
Austrian prisoners of war brought him
to the attention of Life, from which
he resolutely declined a job as staff
photographer in order to maintain his
independence. At the invitation of
Robert Capa, Haas joined Magnum in 1949,
developing close associations with
Capa, Werner Bischof and Henri Cartier-
Bresson. He began experimenting with
color, and in time became the premier
color photographer of the 1950s. In 1962
New York's Museum of Modern Art mounted
its first solo exhibition of his color
work. Haas's books were legion, with The
Creation (1971) selling 350,000 copies.
Haas received the Hasselblad Award in
1986, the year of his death. His books
to date with Steidl are Color Correction
(2011) and On Set (2015).

Abstrakt is a collection of photographs selected by Ernst Haas for a
two-projector 25-minute film he worked on until his death in 1986.
The photographs span his entire career in color from 1952 to 1984.
Many of the photographs were shown in *Life* magazine's fist color issue
devoted to Haas' 1953 story on New York "Images of a Magic City,"
and in his 1962 solo exhibition "Ernst Haas: Color Photography" at the
Museum of Modern Art, the first color retrospective at that institution. The photographs in this book show various abstractions—from
street detritus, to torn posters and other found objects. Haas considered this project to be the culmination of his work in photography.

Ernst Haas was unquestionably one of the best known, most prolific,
and most widely published photographers of the twentieth century.
William A. Ewing

Ernst Haas
Abstrakt

Text by David Campany
Book design by Thomas Lenthal
240 pages
11.8 × 11.8 in. / 29.7 × 29.7 cm
118 color photographs
Four-color process
Clothbound hardcover with dust jacket

€ 50.00 / £ 45.00 / US$ 55.00
ISBN 978-3-95829-393-9

JULIA KRISTEVA, Sorrows and Fugue for the Foreigner (The Silence of Polyphoni), 1991

Come, now! Silence has not only been forced upon you, it is within you: a refusal to speak, a fitful sleep riven to an anguish that wants to remain mute, the private property of your proud and mortified discretion, that silence is a harsh light. Nothing to say, nothingness, no one on the horizon. An impervious fullness: cold diamond, secret treasury, carefully protected, out of reach. Saying nothing, nothing needs to be said, nothing can be said.

It is not the silence of anger that jostles words at the edge of the idea and the mouth; rather, it is the silence that empties the mind and fills the brain with despondency, like the gaze of sorrowful women coiled up in some nonexistant eternity.

INTRODUCTION

ONE HUNDRED WOMEN

The idea for this book came to me many years ago when I discovered the English version of *La femme 100 têtes* by Max Ernst,[1] translated by his wife Dorothea Tanning into *The Hundred Headless Women*, at the famous Strand bookstore in New York. I had always been a great admirer of Ernst's work, and as a young photographer I was strangely struck by the "photographic" quality of the images, which were clearly gravures. It was not that they were readable as photographic images—as "mirrors of reality"—but they were instead rather illustrative, and fascinating in their detail about a world far beyond our imagination, a world that seemed quite violent and mysterious. I later learned these images were collages combining pictures from nineteenth-century wood engravings in popular novels, books on natural science and engraved reproductions of art works. The collages were photographically reproduced before they were printed in book form, hence the impression of being one continuous surface and my initial impression that they were akin to photographs.

However, my book is not about Ernst's book, although it borrows its title and reintroduces parts of André Breton's original introduction. Despite vast differences in artistic and philosophical approaches, the two books "meet" in some instances, and in this text I hope to explain some of the ideas and motivations that after all these years have given me the impetus to realize this project.

DISTANCE AND THE ETERNAL RETURN

Ernst divided his collage-novel into nine chapters, but the events portrayed in the 147 collaged images are not arranged chronologically. It centres on the life of the hero, beginning with his birth and ending with his death and rebirth. Physical violence, riot, crime, war and destruction pervade the images, as the protagonist searches for the wisdom of the hundred headless women. There are direct, and at times ironic references to Dante's journey through Inferno, Purgatory and Paradise and his search for Beatrice in the *Divina Commedia*; however, the two outcomes are quite different.

1
Max Ernst, *The Hundred Headless Woman* (original French title: *La femme 100 têtes*), with an introduction by André Breton; translation and foreword by Dorothea Tanning (New York: George Braziller, first edition, September 1981).

Born in Hamburg in 1952, Angela Grauerholz studied graphic design and literature before moving in 1976 to Montreal where she completed a master's degree in photography at Concordia University. From 1988 to 2017 she was professor of photography and book design at the École de design, Université du Québec. Grauerholz has exhibited at the Kunstverein Hannover, the Albright Knox Art Gallery in Buffalo, the Musée d'art contemporain de Montréal and the National Gallery of Canada, and has participated in events including the Sydney Biennale and documenta IX. In 2006 she received Quebec's Prix Paul-Émile Borduas, in 2014 the Canada Council's Governor General's Award in Visual and Media Arts, and in 2015 the Scotiabank Photography Award published by Steidl.

La femme 100 têtes / The Hundred Headless Woman presents over 150 portraits of 100 women—some acquaintances, some strangers—taken by Angela Grauerholz over a 30-year period and presented for the first time in this book. Collaging diverse photos made with various cameras and technologies with text fragments from a range of mostly female authors, Grauerholz creates a hybrid between a magazine and book that forms a complex portrait of women.

The title *La femme 100 têtes* is borrowed from Max Ernst's 1929 Surrealist collage novel of the same name, in which he combined cut-up and reassembled nineteenth-century illustrations with bizarre captions. Grauerholz welcomes the double entendre of Ernst's title—when read aloud in French it means both "the hundred-headed woman" and "the headless woman"—to create a sense of womanhood intricately individual and violently anonymous. The intentionally quotidian nature of Grauerholz's photos blurs the "class" distinctions between images in an art context, in a printed publication and on the Internet, and tests the changing ways we encounter and judge photography.

Apprehending the face's image becomes a mode of possession. We are surrounded by the image of the woman's face, the obsession of the portrait and the covergirl alike. The face is what belongs to the other. It is unavailable to the woman herself. Susan Stewart

Angela Grauerholz
La femme 100 têtes /
The Hundred Headless Woman

Texts by Angela Grauerholz, André Breton and others
Book design by Elisabeth Charbonneau and Angela Grauerholz
360 pages
9.8 × 13 in. / 24.8 × 33 cm
9 black-and-white and 160 color photographs
Four-color process
Otabind softcover

€ 75.00 / £ 70.00 / US$ 80.00
ISBN 978-3-95829-560-5

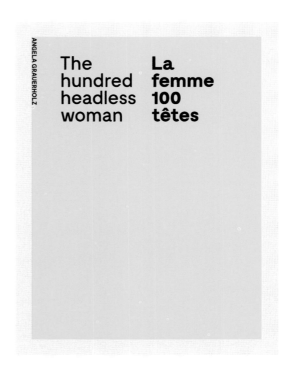

Lucinda Devlin, born in Ann Arbor, Michigan, in 1947, grew up surrounded by the Great Lakes and rural landscapes. Devlin has received numerous awards (including those from the NEA and DAAD) and her work is held in several museums, such as the Guggenheim Museum, the Whitney Museum, and the DZ Bank Collection. Devlin has exhibited throughout the United States and Europe including at the Venice Biennale. Steidl has published her The Omega Suites (2000) and Water Rites (2003).

Lake Pictures is a series of photographs of Lake Huron, one of the Great Lakes bordering the state of Michigan. The pictures—taken at the same place, during the four seasons, and at different times of day and night—explore the changing atmospheric nature of the lake through the prisms of water, sky, color, light, place, space and time. Looking at this immense body of water and the sky above, both initially seem boundless, as if stretching forever into the distance. Only the fine horizon line between the two separates and joins them, pulling us into each photo and reminding us that this sense of infinity is but an intriguing optical fiction.

More than a lake: the *lake, the sea. Devlin's pictures show everything, from a honey-yellow pool to a raging sea; we see the greyish-brown abyss, the opaque, rippling navy blue, a melancholy carpet ... and the slate-like idleness. All this is a result of her morning, midday, evening and nighttime visits to the shoreline. It looks as though the photographer has consulted the Great Lake like an oracle.*
Ulf Erdmann Ziegler

Co-published with Galerie m, Bochum

Lucinda Devlin
Lake Pictures

Texts by Jerry Dennis, Susan Firer, Tom Sherman and Claudia Skutar
Book design by Duncan Whyte / Steidl Design
108 pages
11.7 × 11.6 in. / 29.7 × 29.5 cm
64 color photographs
Four-color process
Hardcover

€ 40.00 / £ 35.00 / US$ 45.00
ISBN 978-3-86930-965-1

Chapter 1: First Pictures

Chapter 2: Termini Beach

Chapter 3: Palermo Unsung / Fans

Chapter 4: Photographers & Weddings

Chapter 5: Catacombs

Chapter 6: Vucciria

Chapter 7: Election Silence

Chapter 8: Prison Graffiti

Chapter 9: Rambo's Taverna

Chapter 10: Massimo & Gino

Chapter 11: Singers TV

Chapter 12: Via Roma

Chapter 13: Son of a Godfather

Born 1968 in Palermo, Mauro D'Agati gained a law degree before beginning to work as a professional photographer in 1995. He initially documented Sicilian jazz festivals, art and theatre events, before contributing to Italian and international magazines. D'Agati's books with Steidl include Palermo Unsung (2009), Alamar (2010), Napule Shot (2010), Sit Lux et Lux Fuit (2012) and Marzia's Family (2015).

Palermo Panorama is Mauro D'Agati's love letter to his beloved hometown, a raw portrait that shows Palermo's charm and grit in equal measure. The book comprises 13 chapters, each dedicated to a distinct series, which all grew organically over time to form a complex picture of the city. Here among others are D'Agati's very first photos, black-and-white street portraits taken while still a student; the waste-littered Termini Beach, a summer destination for the people of Palermo's suburbs; the abandoned and neglected Vucciria neighborhood; portraits of wedding photographers and singers at local music festivals; the Capuchin Catacombs; and transvestites on Via Roma near Palermo's central station. Regardless of his subject, D'Agati portrays Palermo's resilient characters and crumbling beauty with compassion and without judgment.

For many years I've been taking photographs of Palermo and its inhabitants, living side by side with them and using my sense of belonging as an occasional tool. This book is both a declaration of love and an attempt to access the city without fear or favor—a very personal take which I hope unveils the true colors of Palermo.
Mauro D'Agati

Mauro D'Agati
Palermo Panorama

Texts by Mauro D'Agati and Gerhard Steidl
Book design by Mauro D'Agati and Gerhard Steidl
384 pages
8.7 × 11.8 in. / 22 × 30 cm
76 black-and-white and 141 color photographs
Four-color process
Clothbound hardcover

€ 75.00 / £ 70.00 / US$ 85.00
ISBN 978-3-95829-557-5

François-Marie Banier was born in 1947 in Paris. A novelist and playwright, Banier has also been taking photographs of public figures and anonymous people in the street since the 1970s. In 1991 the Centre Pompidou in Paris was the first to display his photography; exhibitions followed in Europe, Asia and America. The Maison Européenne de la Photographie in Paris presented a retrospective in 2003, exhibiting Banier's "written" and "painted" photographs for the first time. His books published by Steidl include Perdre la tête (2006), Beckett (2009) and Never stop dancing (2016).

This book presents François-Marie Banier's portraits of Moroccan construction workers sleeping or at rest in their places of work. Caught in moments of dreaming and escape from their labor, Banier's subjects blend into the soft grey atmosphere of his pictures and seem, if but for a moment, to have escaped the harsher facts of reality. These are candid and tender portraits which continue Banier's practice of photographing strangers he meets in small and large cities. In his words: "To photograph workers asleep on the very ground of their construction site was, once again, to follow the paradoxical lines of being, a solitude embodied in movie heroes who change faces, roles, centuries and sometimes genders, in each of their naps."

It is not the dreamer's spirit only that sleep inhabits. The body in a lying position aligns with the horizon and the dreams that travel across it. My capacity for tenderness overflows: life going to sleep flirts with abandonment, this elegance of any fighter, life being nothing but a battlefield. François-Marie Banier

François-Marie Banier
Tranquille

Text by Erri De Luca
Book design by Martin d'Orgeval, François-Marie Banier and Gerhard Steidl
80 pages
7.1 × 9.6 in. / 18 × 24.5 cm
39 black-and-white photographs
Tritone
Hardcover

€ 35.00 / £ 30.00 / US 40.00
ISBN 978-3-95829-507-0

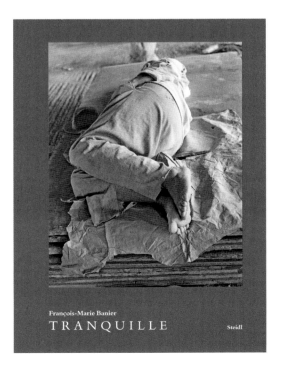

Born in New York City in 1949, Langdon
Clay was raised in New Jersey and Vermont
and attended school in New Hampshire and
Boston. Clay moved to New York in 1971
and spent the next 16 years photographing
there, throughout the US and in Europe
for various magazines and books. In 1987
he moved to Mississippi where he has
since lived and worked with his wife
photographer Maude Schuyler Clay and
their three children. Clay's work is held
in the Victoria and Albert Museum in
London and the Bibliothèque nationale de
France in Paris. Steidl published Clay's
Cars. New York City, 1974–1976 in 2016.

42nd Street, 1979 contains Langdon Clay's 1979 photos of a quintessential strip of 42nd Street near New York's Times Square, showing its
gritty neon charm before it became the more Disney/Las Vegas hub
for theater concoctions that we know today.

Clay recalls the drab and dusty mood in New York City at the end
of the 1970s: the once-exciting political sea change wrought by the
Vietnam War and the Haight Ashbury drug experiment had given way
to a sense of apathy, intensified by the aftermath of an oil crisis and
the lingering Cold War. The particular stretch of 42nd Street between
7th and 8th Avenues had now shifted from the glorious home of gilded
movie palaces of the 1940s to the shadowy site of porn theaters which
many saw as the area's ruin. Yet here real-estate moguls saw potential
to transform this heart of Manhattan into a mecca of tourism, framed
by skyscrapers and shaped by commerce and fast pleasures. "It was
with this coming change written on every wall that I sought to record
for posterity that famous block between 7th and 8th Avenues," says
Clay, "My only regret is that I didn't do the south side of the street."

Night became its own color. Langdon Clay

Langdon Clay
42nd Street, 1979

Text by Langdon Clay
Book design by Steidl Design
128 pages and a gatefold
9.4 x 12.6 in. / 24 x 32 cm
One giant panorama color photograph
Four-color process
Hardcover

€ 75.00 / £ 70.00 / US$ 80.00
ISBN 978-3-95829-281-9

Paul Drake was born in Cheshire in 1974 and Helen File in 1969 in Lancashire. Before meeting they shared an independent and ongoing passion for history and architectural photography. Drake is a self-taught photographer, while File studied photography at Blackpool and the Fylde College; since 2009 they have worked together throughout the United Kingdom and Europe.

This book is the evocative four-year journey of Paul Drake and Helen File into one of the most secretive and heavily fortified borders in the world. For 37 years over 800 watchtowers monitored the surveillance along the Inner German Border; they were the first line of defense against the West and one of the most infamous sites of the Cold War. Continuous games of binocular warfare were carried out by both NATO and the Warsaw Pact across the 500m *Schutzstreifen* or, as it was known in the West, "The Death Strip."

In the ten months between 9 November 1989, when the borders of the German Democratic Republic fell, and the unification of Germany in 1990, over 700 watchtowers were demolished along the Inner German Border. Through meticulous research and with assistance from guards stationed along the border and Berlin Wall, Drake and File have compiled a concise documentation on the watchtowers of the former border. Once an inaccessible and isolated area, the border is now the largest nature reserve in Germany. Drake and File illustrate these remnants of the Cold War in a compelling set of images showing the remaining 75 watchtowers in their current states.

Without the knowledge, guidance and expertise from former members of the Border Troops of the German Democratic Republic, a set of original blueprints, a tape measure and a lot of patience, this project would have been impossible. Paul Drake and Helen File

Paul Drake and Helen File
B-Türme Innerdeutsche Grenze
The Last Watchtowers of the Inner
German Border

Text by Paul Drake and Helen File
Illustrations by Paul Drake
Book design by Steidl Design
272 pages
11.8 × 8.3 in. / 30 × 21 cm
77 color photographs and 106 color illustrations
Four-color process
Hardcover

€ 65.00 / £ 60.00 / US$ 75.00
ISBN 978-3-95829-504-9

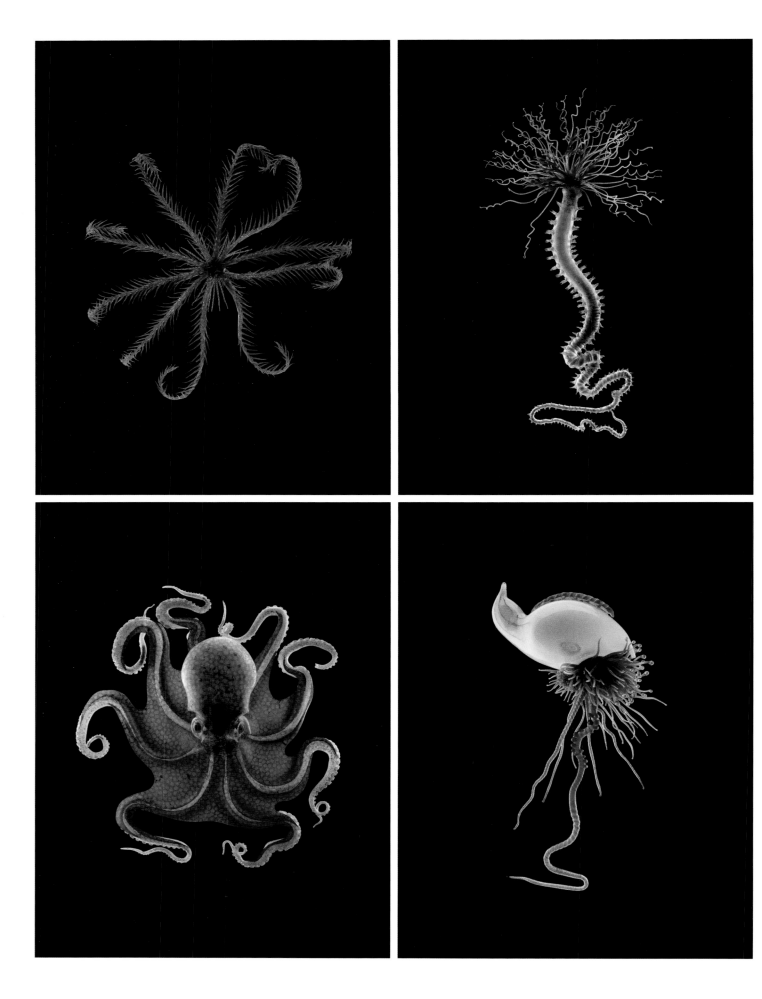

Guido Mocafico was born in Switzerland in 1962, and today works in Switzerland and Paris. A specialist in still lifes, Mocafico's books with Steidl include Venenum (2005), Medusa (2006), Serpens (2007), Movement (2008), Stilleven (2013) and Mocafico Numéro (2016).

Guido Mocafico
Leopold & Rudolf Blaschka
The Marine Invertebrates

Bilingual edition (English / French)
Edited by Patrick Remy
Texts by Alexandra Baudelot, Isabelle Pirotte and Emmanuel G. Reynaud
Book design by Guido Mocafico
320 pages
10.8 × 14 in. / 27.5 × 35.5 cm
252 color photographs
Four-color process
Clothbound hardcover with a tipped-in photograph

€ 75.00 / £ 70.00 / US$ 85.00
ISBN 978-3-95829-398-4

It has long been Guido Mocafico's dream to photograph the master-piece glass models of marine invertebrates and plants that took Leopold (1822–95) and his son Rudolf (1857–1939) Blaschka a lifetime to create. This book fulfills that dream and showcases the Blaschkas' unparalleled dedication to their craft.

Originally from Bohemia but based in Dresden, the Blaschkas worked from the mid-1800s until the 1930s. From clear, colored and painted glass they handmade their intricate models of invertebrate animals (including jellyfish, sea anemones, starfish and sea cucumbers) as well as plants, only on commission and for purposes of study, mainly in Europe and North America. The objects were not sold to the general public and are today held in museum collections including those of Harvard University, the Corning Museum of Glass/Cornell University, and the Natural History Museums in London and Dublin.

It has been a difficult process for Mocafico to gain authorization to photograph the Blaschkas' creations, as most museums do not display these extremely fragile models. Yet Mocafico pursued the largest Blaschka collections throughout Europe and eventually gained access to photograph their hidden treasures in his trademark style. The result is similar to that of his "Nature Morte" series in that we constantly question what we see: a photograph, a painting, the object itself or a product of our imagination?

The Blaschkas spent between 30 and 50 years of each of their lifetimes, day and night, creating their glass models with unbelievable commitment. I was not scared to face the long-term job of photographing their work, and it's since become both an homage and an obsession. Guido Mocafico

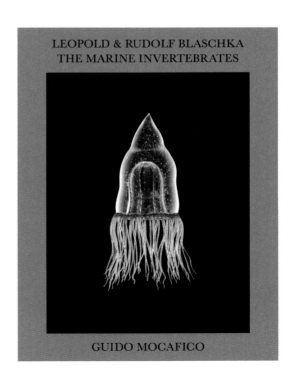

Sze Tsung Nicolás Leong is a British-
American artist, born in Mexico City in
1970. His work is an effort to picture and
understand the complexity of connections
and relationships in the larger world.
His series include "Horizons," "Cities,"
and "History Images" (published by Steidl
in 2005). He is a Guggenheim Fellow,
and his work is held in major museum
collections throughout the world.

On the night of 13 November 2015, Paris was convulsed by a series
of coordinated attacks. Sze Tsung Nicolás Leong, not far from the
strikes, did not consider taking photographs, weighed on not only by
the difficulty of depicting a city already so exhaustively pictured, but
more so by the impossibility of representing such tragedy. The next
day Leong, wandering the city in the aftermath of the events, turned
his camera downward to the ground, focusing on an aspect of the city
we repeatedly look at yet largely do not notice. The resulting photos
render a seemingly known city strange and unfamiliar. At first appearing to be abstractions or even aerials or views of the cosmos, they
reveal specific details we would otherwise miss and which contain
gravity in their apparent banality—from cigarettes left on the asphalt
by mourners, to the footprints and broken glass of the night before,
and the sawdust scattered on the sidewalks soaking up blood.

Paris, Novembre is a portrait of a city at a traumatic moment in its
history and an exploration of how that history leaves its marks on the
city's ground. Leong's series is a gesture of mourning and contemplation, seemingly of nothing and the reluctance to look, yet at the same
time of looking closely and intently.

*In the past, astrologers scrutinized the sky to understand the world.
Leong scrutinizes the ground. Is he also looking to read some message
in these images that he literally picks up from the earth? As if the
ground were the key, the terminus on which all converges.*
Thierry Grillet

Sze Tsung Nicolás Leong
Paris, Novembre

Bilingual edition
English and French
Texts by Thierry Grillet and
Sze Tsung Nicolás Leong
Book design by Sze Tsung Nicolás Leong
56 pages
11.6 × 8 in / 29.5 × 20.4 cm
20 black-and-white photographs
Tritone
Clothbound hardcover

€ 40.00 / £ 35.00 / US$ 45.00
ISBN 978-3-95829-395-3

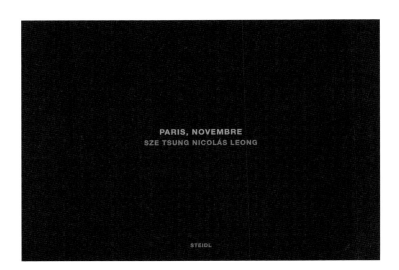

Raised in Williamsburg, Virginia, Sheva Fruitman is a photographer, art director, stylist and designer. After studying art at Bard College in New York State, Fruitman studied photography on the streets of New York City with Lisette Model. Her work has appeared in publications including the New York Times, Condé Nast Traveller, Le Monde and Harper's Bazaar, and is held in many private collections as well as the Victoria and Albert Museum.

Half-Frame Diary: End of the Century presents a selection of photos made between 1998 and 2000 from artist Sheva Fruitman's decades-long photo-diary project. These images idiosyncratically mirror everyday life at the end of the twentieth century, captured by Fruitman as she traveled the world.

Composed as diptychs, the half-frame photos are pairs, with two vertical images in the space of one 35mm frame. Resonances between these sepia-toned streetscapes and interiors link their original contexts and create episodes from layered, incomplete narratives: be it bunches of ripe bananas played against a tarot reader's neon sign of a palm, changing reflections in a shop window, or the linear patterns of buildings and a cherry picker versus those of a subway platform. These once timeless scenes, now published for the first time, are remnants of a not-too-distant world that no longer exists.

Always be on the lookout for the presence of wonder. E. B. White

Sheva Fruitman
Half-Frame Diary
End of the Century

Text by Sheva Fruitman
Book design by Sheva Fruitman and Gerhard Steidl
184 pages
9 × 12 in. / 22.9 × 30.5 cm
200 sepia photographs
Four-color process
Hardcover

€ 45.00 / £ 40.00 / US$ 50.00
ISBN 978-3-95829-499-8

SHEVA FRUITMAN

HALF-FRAME DIARY:
END OF THE CENTURY

STEIDL

Born in Lancashire in 1942, Andy Summers
has enjoyed a prolific career since his
time as the guitarist with rock band
The Police in the 1980s. In the eye
of these experiences and influenced
by Robert Frank, Ralph Gibson and Lee
Freidlander, Summers became a dedicated
photographer. To date he has published
four photobooks including Throb (1983)
and I'll be Watching You: Inside The
Police 1980-83 (2007), and held more than
40 international exhibitions.

Andy Summers
The Bones of Chuang Tzu

Text by Andy Summers
Book design by Andy Summers and Gerhard Steidl
120 pages
9 × 12 in. / 22.9 × 30.5 cm
80 black-and-white photographs
Tritone
Hardcover

€ 40.00 / £ 35.00 / US$ 50.00
ISBN 978-3-95829-403-5

The Bones of Chuang Tzu is Andy Summer's interpretation of China.
Influenced by many aspects of Asian culture since his teenage
years and particularly the writings of fourth-century Chinese poet,
philosopher and disciple of the wandering life Chuang Tzu, this book
is a logical culmination of these interests. Rather than a collection
of standard pictures of China, Summers uses the backdrop of the
country to explore its symbolic and poetic tropes as he sees them,
finding the unique lines, shapes and textures that repeat and represent that civilization in metaphoric terms—thus we find the lotus, the
brushstroke, the dragon.

Summer focuses on aspects of China that are rapidly disappearing.
Yet rather than romanticizing the past and seeing photography as an
act of preservation, his pictures gesture towards the specific vitality
of a culture. Take for example, Summer's photos of the Naxi orchestra
in western China, through which he felt like he knew all these old
musicians, but returning a year later he was dismayed to see many
had passed on. "I found myself no longer shooting everything that
confronted me," says Summers, "but rather slicing out pieces of
my environment that would express something other: photographs
as haiku. From Shanghai to Tibet, *The Bones of Chuang Tzu* reflects
what happened."

*With the same poetry and depth of his music, Andy's photographs
from China show us his delicate visual regard. We hear what he is
seeing.* Ralph Gibson

Exhibitions: Le Pavillion Montpellier, February 2019

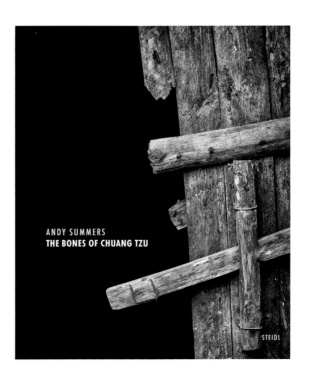

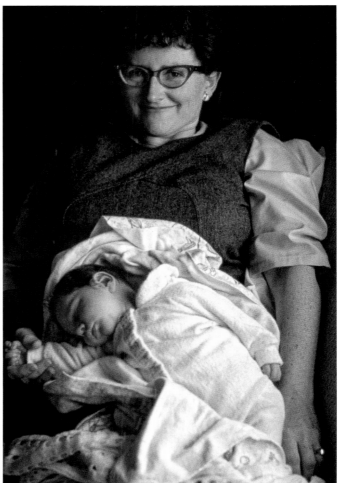

Marq Sutherland, born in San Diego, California, in 1974, grew up in an artistic family. In 1998 he became assistant to contemporary landscape painter Woody Gwen and began his photographic studies with David Scheinbaum and Steve Fitch at the College of Santa Fe, graduating in 2001 with a self-designed Bachelor of Arts in photography, music and technology. He continued his studies with Jack Fulton at the San Francisco Art Institute receiving a Master of Fine Arts in 2005. Sutherland was a finalist for the 2002 Willard Van Dyke Award, and received a SFAI Teaching Assistantship Award in 2004 and a Helen Wurlitzer Foundation Fellowship in 2008. He lives and works in Bilbao, Spain.

Pilgrim is a visual journey into one woman's life through the eyes of her parents, husband and son. In her last years, Marq Sutherland returned home to help his mother through this time during which they spoke about a recurring subject—her past. Years before, Pilgrim had given him his maternal grandfather's and father's photographic negatives. Sifting through thousands of images unseen for decades, Sutherland found many photographs which depicted his mother's life from the moment of birth, and saw how he might complete her story with love and dignity—how they both might hold onto life as they learned to let go.

For me, this book has become both a way to honor the life of my mother, Pilgrim Sutherland, and to connect and collaborate with my grandparents, Poul de Hoffmann and Elsie Boote de Hoffmann, and my father Frank Sutherland through the images they left behind.
Marq Sutherland

Marq Sutherland
Pilgrim

Book design by Marq Sutherland and Gerhard Steidl
Three volumes, 240 pages
5.1 × 8.3 in. / 13 × 21 cm

Vol. 1: Daughter
80 pages
59 photographs

Vol. 2: Wife
80 pages
51 photographs

Vol. 3: Mother
80 pages
66 photographs

Four-color process
Three softcover books in a slipcase

€ 48.00 / £ 45.00 / US$ 65.00
ISBN 978-3-86930-695-7

Slipcase

Volume 1

Volume 2

Volume 3

Koto Bolofo was born in South Africa in 1959 and raised in Great Britain. Bolofo has photographed for magazines such as Vogue, Vanity Fair and GQ, and made short films for the Berlinale and the Venice Film Festival. He has created advertising campaigns for companies including Hermès, Christian Dior, Louis Vuitton and Dom Pérignon. Bolofo's books with Steidl include Venus (2008), Horse Power (2010), I Spy with My Little Eye, Something Beginning with S (2010), Vroom! Vroom! (2010), La Maison (2011) and The Prison (2014).

Hahnemühle is the oldest paper mill in Germany — and indeed the world — which has consistently produced fine art paper since its inception over 400 years ago. Using their own supply of spring water and imported pulps, Hahnemühle crafts luxury papers based on time-tested traditional methods. In *Paper Making,* Koto Bolofo graphically captures Hahnemühle's artisanal processes and antique machinery alongside today's most advanced technologies, uncovering the attention to detail, vision and pride that have sustained the company's unmatched reputation for centuries.

Koto Bolofo
Paper Making

Texts by Koto Bolofo
and Gerhard Steidl
Book design by Koto Bolofo
and Gerhard Steidl
160 pages
11.4 × 14.6 in. / 29 × 37 cm
148 black-and-white photographs
Quadratone
Clothbound hardcover

€ 50.00 / £ 45.00 / US$ 60.00
ISBN 978-3-86930-637-7

Koto Bolofo was born in South Africa in 1959 and raised in Great Britain. Bolofo has photographed for magazines such as Vogue, Vanity Fair and GQ, and made short films for the Berlinale and the Venice Film Festival. He has created advertising campaigns for companies including Hermès, Christian Dior, Louis Vuitton and Dom Pérignon. Bolofo's books with Steidl include Venus (2008), Horse Power (2010), I Spy with My Little Eye, Something Beginning with S (2010), Vroom! Vroom! (2010), La Maison (2011) and The Prison (2014).

This whimsical and in-depth behind-the-scenes study leads the reader into the world of Steidl Publishers in Göttingen. With his inimitable and patient eye, Koto Bolofo takes us through the labyrinthine corridors and stairways of the publishing house, documenting the myriad processes and people at work, and giving us an insider's glance into how Steidl's books come to life.

Koto Bolofo
Printing

Text by Koto Bolofo
Book design by Koto Bolofo
and Gerhard Steidl
With a video by Koto Bolofo on DVD
80 pages
11.4 × 12.6 in. / 29 × 37 cm
130 color photographs
Four-color process
Clothbound hardcover

€ 50.00 / £ 45.00 / US$ 60.00
ISBN 978-3-86930-636-0

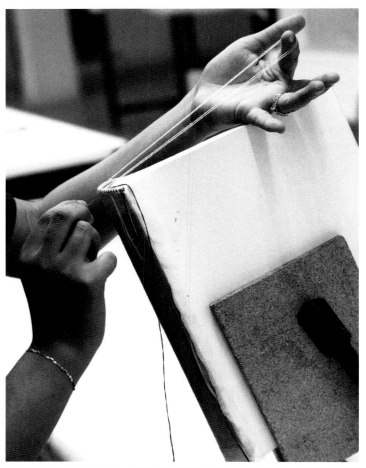

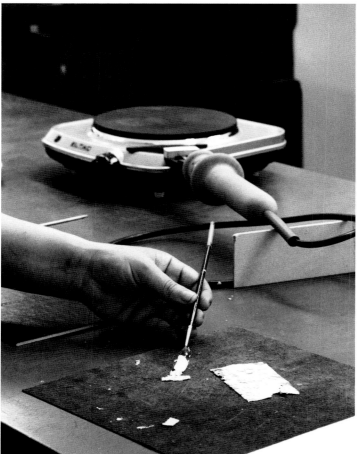

Koto Bolofo was born in South Africa in 1959 and raised in Great Britain. Bolofo has photographed for magazines such as Vogue, Vanity Fair and GQ, and made short films for the Berlinale and the Venice Film Festival. He has created advertising campaigns for companies including Hermès, Christian Dior, Louis Vuitton and Dom Pérignon. Bolofo's books with Steidl include Venus (2008), Horse Power (2010), I Spy with My Little Eye, Something Beginning with S (2010), Vroom! Vroom! (2010), La Maison (2011) and The Prison (2014).

Koto Bolofo creases book spines and gently flicks through pages to explore what has happened behind the scenes in the world of bookbinding—an ancient craft that has protected our most valuable manuscripts since the infancy of art and literature, keeping safe the wisdom of the past. As the processes of binding have now increasingly moved from man to machine, Bolofo's *Binding* is a meticulous study of bookbinding today that embraces the new and laments the loss of the old. The human touch is still evident, but is gradually disappearing. Trying to hold back the tides of time, Bolofo playfully begs the question: has this cherished practice lost its soul and are we now slaves to the machine?

To bind books is to do the impossible. Koto Bolofo

Koto Bolofo
Binding

Text by Koto Bolofo
Book design by Koto Bolofo
and Gerhard Steidl
80 pages
11.4 × 12.6 in. / 29 × 37 cm
80 photographs
Quadratone
Clothbound hardcover

€ 50.00 / £ 45.00 / US$ 60.00
ISBN 978-3-86930-635-3

Anish Kapoor was born in 1954 in Mumbai. Between 1973 and '78 he studied Fine Art at Hornsey College of Art, then at the Chelsea School of Art. He represented Britain at the 44th Venice Biennale and won the Turner Prize in 1991. Solo exhibitions and public commissions include Tate Modern (2002); Royal Academy (2009); Cloud Gate, Millennium Park, Chicago (2004); Grand Palais, Paris (2011); Orbit, Olympic Park (2012); Martin-Gropius-Bau (2013) and Chateau du Versailles (2015). Kapoor lives and works in London.

The powerful religious sites of Uluru and Kata Tjuta in the Northern Territory of Australia have been of deep interest to the artist Anish Kapoor since he first visited them in the 1980s. At Uluru he found a landscape of monumental scale which contained intimate and ritually resonant sites. A landscape of hollows and voids which he has read as resonant of primal or even "original" structure. Kapoor describes Uluru as "an object with a perforated skin which lends itself to mythic meaning."

On his visit in 1991, Kapoor noted in his sketchbook "a white bump on a white wall." He later made the sculpture *When I am Pregnant* (1992), describing it as "an object in a state of becoming." The idea of the proto-object is central to Kapoor's work. In 2012 Kapoor returned to Uluru and Kata Tjuta. These two photographic volumes trace his journey. They reveal through his eyes the artist's pre-occupation with form and pre-form, skin and surface in relation to deep interior.

Unbelievable things revealed themselves every day. I felt deeply connected with the place, and with a kind of possible interpretation, a symbolic interpretation of the holes and the strips of stone that seem to be leaning against it. I was amazed, not at the monolith, but at the way the monolith seemed to be made up of symbolic events.
Anish Kapoor

Anish Kapoor
Uluru & Kata Tjuta Photographs

Edited by Anish Kapoor Studio
Book design by Brighten the Corners
5.5 × 8.1 in. / 14 × 20.5 cm

Vol. 1: Uluru
584 pages
278 color photographs

Vol. 2: Kata Tjuta
168 pages
84 color photographs

Four-color process
Two hardcover books in a slipcase

€ 125.00 / £ 100.00 / US$ 150.00
ISBN 978-3-95829-260-4

Slipcase

Volume 1: Uluru

Volume 2: Kata Tjuta

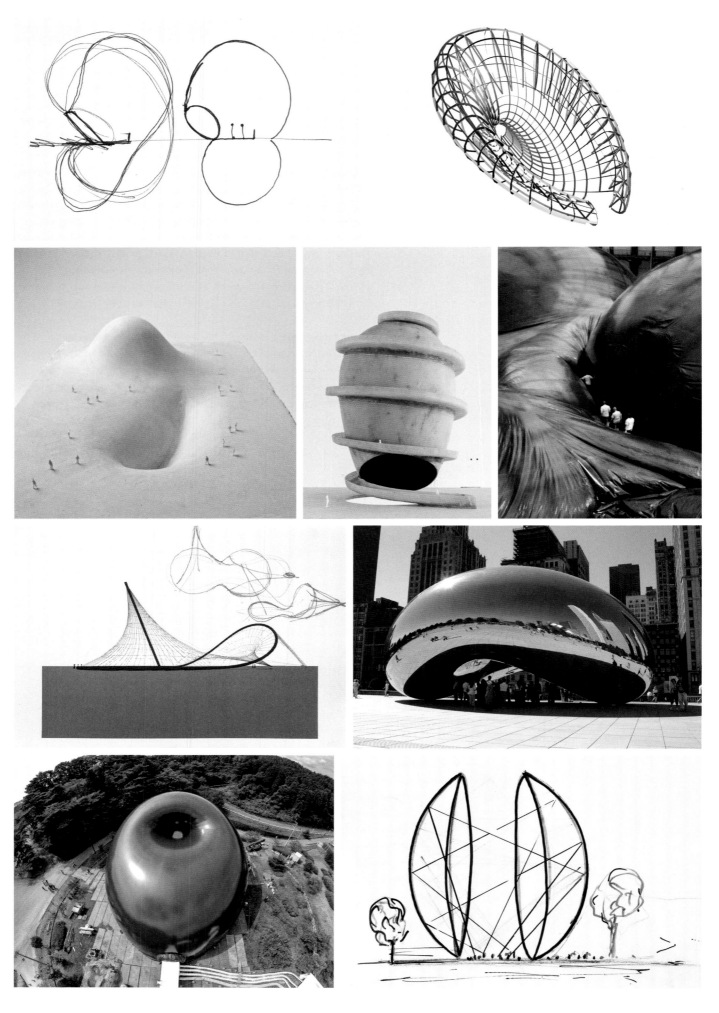

Anish Kapoor was born in 1954 in Mumbai. Between 1973 and 1978 he studied Fine Art at Hornsey College of Art, then at the Chelsea School of Art. Kapoor represented Britain at the 44th Venice Biennale and won the Turner Prize in 1991. Solo exhibitions and public commissions include Tate Modern (2002); Royal Academy (2009); Cloud Gate, Millennium Park, Chicago (2004); Grand Palais, Paris (2011); Orbit, Olympic Park (2012); Martin-Gropius-Bau (2013) and Chateau du Versailles (2015). Kapoor lives and works in London.

This publication brings together for the first time Anish Kapoor's architectural projects and ideas that span the last 40 years. These are concepts that continue to inform all areas of Kapoor's artistic output, many of which have been realized in works that confound the distinctions between art and architecture, pushing architecture into radical new territory.

Kapoor's projects renegotiate the relationship not only between art and architecture but also between the very sense of space within ourselves and that of the external world. The forms he presents to us create spaces that blur the duality of subject and object, of interior and exterior. Monochrome fields of color, mirrored surfaces and fathomless voids all destabilize our place in the world. The more than 2,000 sketches, models, renderings and plans in this book show the journey of these forms to how they might exist in reality as well as the spaces they inhabit or create, both outside and within us.

For a long time before—even from the pigment pieces—I'd been thinking of my work as potential architecture. I've always been convinced by the idea that to make new art you have to make new space.
Anish Kapoor

Anish Kapoor
Make New Space
Architectural Projects

Edited by Anish Kapoor Studio
Book design by Brighten the Corners
6.9 × 9.4 in. / 17.5 × 24 cm

Vol. 1
600 pages
1,053 color photographs and images

Vol. 2
592 pages
1,053 color photographs and images

Four-color process
Two hardcover books in a sleeve

€ 250.00 / £ 200.00 / US$ 300.00
ISBN 978-3-95829-420-2

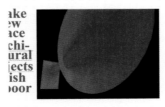

Sleeve   Volume 1   Volume 2

Born in Strasbourg, Tomi Ungerer (1931-
2019), failed his final school exams
yet subsequently hitchhiked throughout
Europe and published his first drawings
in the legendary Simplicissimus magazine.
He began his extensive career as an
illustrator, children's book author and
artist in New York. In 2003 Ungerer
was appointed the first Ambassador for
Childhood and Education by the Council
of Europe, and in 2007 the Tomi Ungerer
Museum opened in Strasbourg, making
him the first living artist with a
museum dedicated to his life and work
in France. In 2014 he received France's
National Order of Merit, and in 2018 he
was appointed Commandeur de la Legion
d'Honneur by French president Emmanuel
Macron.

This extravagant book presents 330 of Tomi Ungerer's illustrations, paintings and collages, many of them previously unpublished. When Ungerer moved from the Alsace to New York in the mid-1950s and began working as a graphic designer and illustrator, a crazy new world opened itself up to him, which the gifted artist transformed into what are perhaps the most remarkable and powerful works of his career—expressive and universal pictures that present the land of opportunity in an inimitable manner.

Tomi Ungerer's work is record-breaking.
Frankfurter Allgemeine Sonntagszeitung

Co-published with Diogenes, Zurich

Tomi Ungerer
America

Edited by Philipp Keel
Foreword by Tomi Ungerer
Afterword by Philipp Keel
Book design by Kobi Benezri and Philipp Keel
416 pages
11 x 14.4 in. / 28 x 36.5 cm
330 color images
Four-color process
Clothbound hardcover

€ 85.00 / £ 80.00 / US$ 95.00
ISBN 978-3-95829-574-2

**TOMI
UNGERER
AMERICA**

STEIDL·DIOGENES

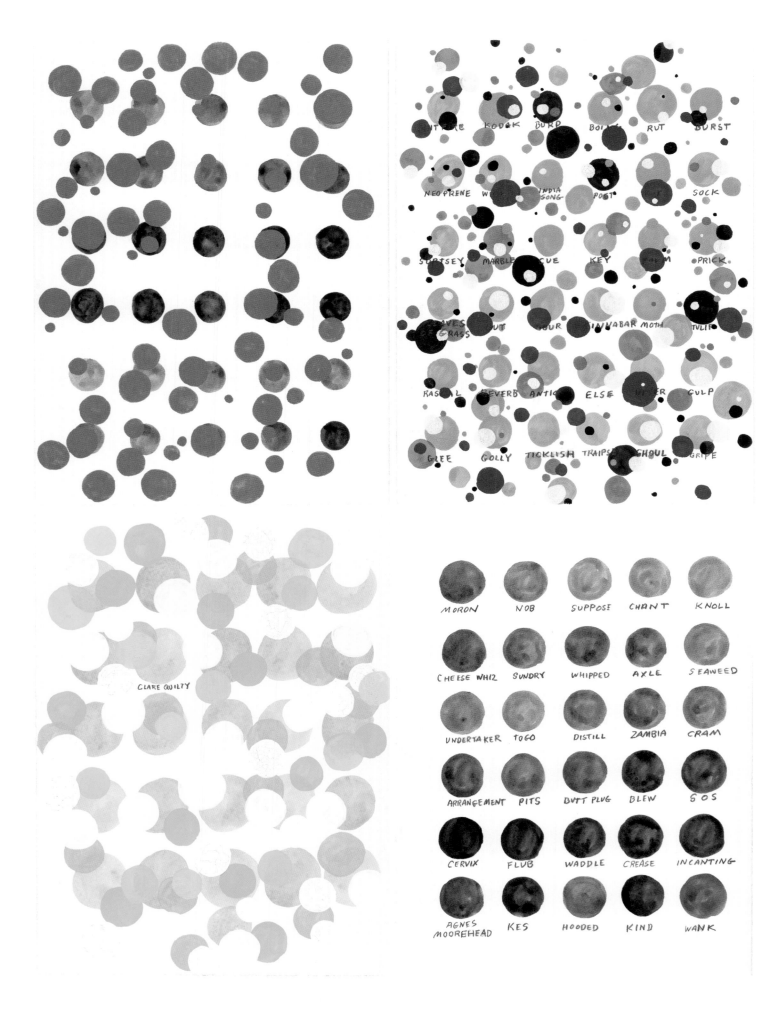

CLARE QUILTY

KODAK BURP RUT BURST

NEOPRENE INDIA SONG POST SOCK

SURTSEY MARBLE CUE KEY PRICK

SEA GRASS SOUR CINNABAR MOTH TULIP

RASCAL REVERB ANTIC ELSE GULP

GLEE GOLLY TICKLISH TRAIPSE GHOUL GRIPE

MORON	NOB	SUPPOSE	CHANT	KNOLL
CHEESE WHIZ	SUNDRY	WHIPPED	AXLE	SEAWEED
UNDERTAKER	TOGO	DISTILL	ZAMBIA	CRAM
ARRANGEMENT	PITS	BUTT PLUG	BLEW	SOS
CERVIX	FLUB	WADDLE	CREASE	INCANTING
AGNES MOOREHEAD	KES	HOODED	KIND	WANK

Roni Horn was born in New York in 1955. Horn's oeuvre focuses on conceptually-based photography, sculpture, books and drawing. Recent solo exhibitions include those at Tate Modern, Whitney Museum of American Art, Centre Pompidou, Kunsthalle Bregenz, Kunsthalle Hamburg, Kunsthalle Basel, Fundació Joan Miró, De Pont Foundation and Fondation Beyeler. Horn's books with Steidl include bird (2008), aka (2010), Hack Wit (2015) and Th Rose Prblm (2016).

"Remembered Words" is the title of a series of watercolors Roni Horn created in 2013 and 2014. An important part of Horn's work revolves around language. In this series she literally engages in remembering words and pairs them with dots, adding the words to the dots like footnotes or captions, creating a kind of personal, even autobiographical form. The combination of the dots—which are sometimes arranged in color-coordinated rows, on other drawings random and overlapping, wild and out of control—with the words creates unexpected relations and meanings, endless strings of associations, absurd and beautiful at the same time.

Roni Horn
Remembered Words

Book design by Roni Horn
296 pages
10.25 × 14 in. / 26 × 35.5 cm
296 color images
Four-color process
Clothbound hardcover

€ 85.00 / £ 75.00 / US$ 95.00
ISBN 978-3-86930-996-5

Hannah Collins was born in London in 1956. From 1989 to 2010 she lived and worked in Barcelona, and today lives between London and Almeria, Spain. Collins has received many awards including a Fulbright Scholarship and was nominated for the Turner Prize in 1993. In 2015 a retrospective of her work was shown at the Sprengel Museum Hannover, in conjunction with the award of the Spectrum Prize. In addition to the Hannover retrospective publication, Collins' last book was The Fragile Feast (2011). She has completed a recent body of work in Japan and has ongoing projects in Amazonia and the American South.

Noah Purifoy (1917-2004) moved to Los Angeles in 1953 and enrolled as the first African-American student at what is now the California Institute of the Arts. Purifoy graduated with a BFA just before his fortieth birthday. With fellow artist Judson Powell he organized the exhibition "66 Signs of Neon" with material salvaged from the Watts Rebellion. He co-founded the Watts Towers Arts Center, and initiated various programs to bring art into the prison system. The Noah Purifoy Outdoor Sculpture Museum is situated near Joshua Tree in the Mojave Desert.

Hannah Collins
Noah Purifoy

Edited with Mark Holborn
Text by Hannah Collins
Book design by Hannah Collins (following Walker Evans' book Message from the Interior)
44 pages
13.8 × 14.5 in. / 35 × 36.7 cm
18 black-and-white photographs
Quadratone
Clothbound hardcover

€ 75.00 / £ 68.00 / US$ 85.00
ISBN 978-3-95829-268-0

Though born in Snow Hill, Alabama in 1917, Noah Purifoy lived most of his life in Los Angeles and Joshua Tree, California, where he died in 2004. The exhibition of his work, *Junk Dada*, at LACMA in 2015 as well as the recent publication by Steidl of his notebooks and essays in *High Desert*, have contributed to the legacy of this long-overlooked artist who first came to prominence with sculpture assembled from the debris of the Watts Rebellion of 1965.

In the last 15 years of his life Purifoy lived in the Mojave Desert where he created large-scale sculptures spread over ten acres. On visiting this site Hannah Collins made a series of exquisite black-and-white photographic studies of Purifoy's work. Her rigorous aesthetic stance is unwittingly reminiscent of the formality of Walker Evans, who would have greatly appreciated Purifoy's transformation of discarded materials into grand yet vernacular forms.

Message from the Interior, Walker Evans' photographic study of 1966, which through the selection of a handful of pictures of interiors suggests a wide and disparate landscape, became a model for the publication of Collins' work from Purifoy's site. Her 18 photographs are presented here in a format that exactly echoes Evans' publication, both typographically and spatially. The intention is not imitative, but refers to the grandeur and scale achieved by Purifoy. Cumulatively his work becomes a transitory monument inevitably destined to decay into the desert itself.

I do not wish to be an artist. I only wish that art enables me to be.
Noah Purifoy

Jim Dine

Asia 8

Japan 8

Damien Hirst

Anna Atkins

Adolphe de Meyer

Hans/Jean Arp

Volker Heinze

Richard Serra

Limited Editions

How does one recreate the virtuosic charcoal lines drawn by Richard Serra in his sketchbooks, to capture not just their appearance but somehow their spirit? How to replicate in offset printing the delicate collotypes on vellum of Adolphe de Meyer's 1914 *Le Prélude à l'après-midi d'un faune*? How to craft book objects that match Damien Hirst's ambition to photograph every dispensing pharmacy in Greater London, or Jim Dine's dream to make a book a day for an entire year?

All these questions and more we seek to answer in our limited editions. Limited perhaps in their smaller print-runs, they are unlimited in terms of the time and resources we invest in their realization. These multiples in book form intricately embody the artists' intentions, and put the imaginations and capabilities of all of us at Steidl to the test. We hope you enjoy our unlimited limited editions.

  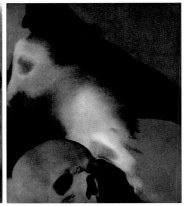

Birds

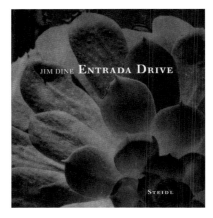  

Entrada Drive

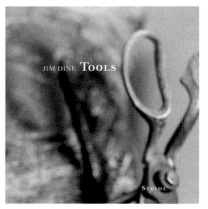 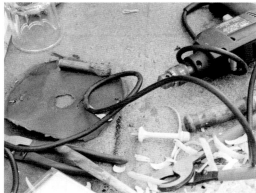 

Tools

Signed and numbered self-portrait

Born in 1935 in Cincinnati, Ohio, Jim
Dine completed a Bachelor of Fine Arts
at Ohio University in 1957 and has since
become one of the most profound and
prolific contemporary artists. Dine's
unparalleled career spans 60 years, and
his work is held in numerous private
and public collections. His books with
Steidl include Pinocchio (2006), Hot
Dream (52 Books) (2008), A Printmaker's
Document (2013) and Paris Reconnaissance
(2018).

Jim Dine
3 Cats and a Dog (Self-portrait)

Limited edition of 50 sets

Text by Jim Dine
Book design by Jim Dine, Diana Michener and Gerhard
Steidl
11.6 × 12.4 in. / 29.5 × 31.5 cm
Tritone
Three clothbound hardcovers with dust jackets,
together with an etching printed over a stone
lithograph on 360 g Fabriano paper signed and
numbered by Jim Dine, all in a slipcase

Birds
88 pages
36 black-and-white photographs
Clothbound hardcover with dust jacket
and Japanese folds

Entrada Drive
96 pages
44 black-and-white photographs
Clothbound hardcover with dust jacket

Tools
96 pages
43 black-and-white and 1 color photographs
Clothbound hardcover with dust jacket

€ 300.00 / £ 250.00 / US$ 350.00
ISBN 978-3-95829-611-4

3 Cats and a Dog (Self-portrait) comprises three photobooks by
Jim Dine—*Birds* (2001), *Entrada Drive* (2005) and *Tools* (2017)—with
a signed self-portrait etching printed over a lithograph. Regardless
of his subject, Dine's photography is simultaneously a record of his
immediate environment and a form of autobiography shaped by
remembrance. The protagonists of *Birds* are the white owl, symbol
of innocence, and its jester-like companion the black crow, who
inhabited Dine's Berlin studio in the winter of 1996. *Entrada Drive*
transports us to the silvery abundance of Los Angeles flora: the great
succulents, fans of grass and proud birds of paradise encountered by
Dine and his wife Diana Michener on their walks around their garden
and to the Pacific Ocean while staying at 234 Entrada Drive in early
2001. Finally, we return to Dine's studio in photos of the tools with
which he makes art—paintbrushes, drills, hammers, pliers, scissors,
saws, clamps and more. *Tools* is both an unfiltered look into Dine's
working space and his ode to the beauty of the tools themselves, a
love born in childhood when he explored his grandfather's hardware
store, admiring the grit, gleaming ceramic sinks, and color charts,
in his words like "perfect, perfect jewel boxes." Dine's self-portrait
rounds off this collection, his eyes fixing us, as his camera fixes its
subject.

*I keep going because, like the woman who swallowed the knives and
nails, I can't stop.* Jim Dine

Slipcase

Lithograph (limited edition of 50)

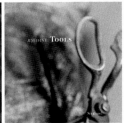

Book: Birds   Book: Entrada Drive   Book: Tools

Steidl
BOOK
AWARDS

ASIA 8 (2016/19)

COLLECTOR'S SET WRAPPED FUROSHIKI STYLE

Gwen Lee (ed.)
Asia 8

Limited edition of 500 sets
Packaging design by Theseus Chan
8 books wrapped furoshiki style

€ 300.00 / £ 270.00 / US$ 350.00
ISBN 978-3-95829-368-7

Steidl
BOOK
AWARDS

JAPAN 8 (2016/19)

COLLECTOR'S SET WRAPPED FUROSHIKI STYLE

My role in *Asia 8* and *Japan 8* is to forge a strong graphic identity for the projects. This includes creating their boxed sets—wrapped furoshiki style—as well as other printed matters that accompany the individual artists' books. Together with Gwen Lee, Yusuke Nakajima and Gerhard Steidl, I also assist and give advice to the artists in drafting and designing their books. Collaborating closely with all the

190

Yusuke Nakajima (ed.)
Japan 8

Limited edition of 500 sets
Packaging design by Theseus Chan
8 books wrapped furoshiki style

€ 300.00 / £ 270.00 / US$ 350.00
ISBN 978-3-95829-425-7

Book 1:
Satoshi Hirano
Reconstruction
Shibuya, 2014-2017

Book 2:
Gentaro Ishizuka
Gold Rush Alaska

Book 3:
Toru Komatsu
A Distant Shore

Book 4:
Toshiaki Mori
B, drawings of abstract forms

Book 5:
Tomoyuki Sagami
YKTO

Book 6:
Tatsuo Suzuki
Friction / Tokyo Streets

Book 7:
Toshiya Watanabe
Thereafter

Book 8:
Takumi Hasegawa
When Takumi Met the
Legends of the World

artists in Göttingen has been fulfilling and satisfying to say the least. We hope you will take the time to savor the subtle qualities of these books—the smell of printed ink, the textures of the papers and binding materials—and be as inspired by them as we are.
Theseus Chan, Art Director

Vol. 1: Barking & Dagenham, Barnet, Bexley

Vol. 3: City of London, Croydon, Ealing

Vol. 7: Kingston upon Thames, Lambeth, Lewisham, Merton

Vol. 10: Wandsworth, Westminster

Born in Bristol in 1965, British artist
Damien Hirst employs a varied practice
of installation, sculpture, painting
and drawing to explore the relationships
between art, religion, science, life and
death. Iconic works include The Physical
Impossibility of Death in the Mind of
Someone Living (1991) and For the Love
of God (2007). Hirst won the Turner Prize
in 1995.

Damien Hirst
Pharmacy London

Limited edition of 750 boxed sets

Book design by Jason Beard
3,820 pages
18 × 12 in. / 45.7 x 30.5 cm
3,565 color photographs
Four-color process
Ten clothbound hardcovers, each in a
cardboard slipcase, housed in a wooden crate

Vol. 1
Barking & Dagenham, Barnet, Bexley
344 pages

Vol. 2
Brent, Bromley, Camden
416 pages

Vol. 3
City of London, Croydon, Ealing
324 pages

Vol. 4
Enfield, Greenwich, Hackney, Hammersmith & Fulham
420 pages

Vol. 5
Haringey, Harrow, Havering
344 pages

Vol. 6
Hillingdon, Hounslow, Islington, Kensington & Chelsea
420 pages

Vol. 7
Kingston upon Thames, Lambeth, Lewisham, Merton
384 pages

Vol. 8
Newham, Redbridge, Richmond upon Thames
344 pages

Vol. 9
Southwark, Sutton, Tower Hamlets
436 pages

Vol. 10
Wandsworth, Westminster
388 pages

€ 800.00 / £ 700.00 / US$ 950.00
ISBN 978-3-86930-991-0

In 2005 Damien Hirst began photographing every dispensing pharmacy
in the Greater London area. Shooting both the individual pharmacists
behind their counters and the exterior views of the city's 1,832
chemists, the project has taken over a decade to complete. The
images are brought together in their entirety in this extraordinary
ten-volume artist's book, which presents a portrait of the city
through the people and places that prescribe the medicines we take
on a habitual and daily basis.

Hirst's career-long obsession with the minimalist aesthetics employed
by pharmaceutical companies—the cool colors and simple geometric
forms—first manifested in his series of Medicine Cabinets, conceived
in 1988 while still at Goldsmiths College. For his 1992 installation
Pharmacy Hirst recreated an entire chemist within the gallery space,
stating: "I've always seen medicine cabinets as bodies, but also like
a cityscape or civilization, with some sort of hierarchy within it.
[*Pharmacy*] is also like a contemporary museum. In a hundred years it
will look like an old apothecary." *Pharmacy London* similarly embodies
the artist's realization of an "idea of a moment in time." The publication also, however, reads as a distilled expression of Hirst's continuing
belief in the near-religious role medicine plays in our society.

*What's always got me is that people's belief in their drugs is so
unquestionable.* Damien Hirst

Vol. 1   Vol. 2   Vol. 3

Vol. 4   Vol. 5   Vol. 6

Vol. 7   Vol. 8   Vol. 9

Vol. 10

Rhodomenia laciniata.

Alaria esculenta.

Haloseris polypodioides.

Asperococcus pusillus.

Cystoseira ericoides.

Fucus Mackaii.

Laminaria bulbosa.

Chylocladia clavellosa.

Sargassum plumosum.

194

The first photobook ever.

Anna Atkins (1799-1871) came of age in
Victorian England and lived much of her
life at Halstead Place in Kent. After
producing Photographs of British Algæ,
she collaborated with her friend Anne
Dixon to create striking cyanotypes of
ferns, feathers and flowering plants. In
addition to The New York Public Library,
choice holdings of her photographs can be
found the collections such as those of
the Royal Society in London, the Linnean
Society, the J. Paul Getty Museum, the
Rijksmuseum and the Jardin des Plantes
in Paris.

Anna Atkins
Photographs of British Algæ:
Cyanotype Impressions
(Sir John Herschel's Copy)

Limited edition of 1,000 boxed sets

Texts by Joshua Chuang and Larry J. Schaaf
7.9 × 9.4 in. / 20 × 24 cm
239 cyanotypes
Quadratone
13 softcover books housed in an archive box

Part I: 24 pages   Part VIII: 26 pages
Part II: 26 pages   Part IX: 26 pages
Part III: 26 pages   Part X: 26 pages
Part IV: 26 pages   Part XI: 26 pages
Part V: 26 pages   Part XII: 26 pages
Part VI: 26 pages   Part XIII: 154 pages
Part VII: 26 pages

€ 500.00 / £ 450.00 / US$ 650.00
ISBN 978-3-95829-510-0

Shortly after William Henry Fox Talbot announced his invention of
photography in 1839, the dedicated amateur botanist Anna Atkins,
daughter of a prominent British scientist, began to experiment with
the new medium. In 1843 she turned to her friend Sir John Herschel's
recently discovered cyanotype process to publish her growing
collection of native seaweeds—a daring way to introduce photography
into book illustration. At regular intervals over the next decade, Atkins
printed and issued these bracingly modern, deeply-hued photograms
to her "botanical friends" in the form of hand-stitched fascicles
of a book she entitled *Photographs of British Algæ: Cyanotype
Impressions*.

The first book to be illustrated by photography and the earliest
sustained application of photography to science, *British Algæ* is a
landmark in the histories of publishing and photography. Of the nearly
two dozen substantially complete or partial copies known to exist,
each is distinct in its appearance and often in its number and arrangement of plates. The set of 13 parts she gave to Sir John Herschel—now
in the Spencer Collection of The New York Public Library—is especially
important and was carefully preserved by generations of the Herschel
family exactly as Sir John received it. This sumptuous facsimile edition
reproduces the recto and verso of each plate, presenting the work as
its creator intended: as bound volumes to lingered over, studied and
admired, page by extraordinary page.

*Rarely revealing any hint of their 175-year-old age, these cyanotypes
look as if Anna just handed them to us, preserving a distant past while
simultaneously offering a contemporary point of view.* Larry J. Schaaf

Co-published with The New York Public Library

Part I   Part II   Part III   Part IV

Part V   Part VI   Part VII   Part VIII

Part IX   Part X   Part XI   Part XII

Part XIII

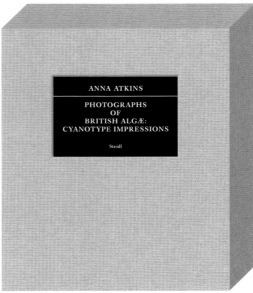

Clamshell box

REPRODUCTIONS
de
TRENTE PHOTOGRAPHIES
de
Monsieur
le Baron A. DE MEYER.

Suivies
de quelques pages
d'Auguste Rodin, de Jacques–Emile
Blanche et de Jean Cocteau.

Vous dansez! voici votre lot.

Le secret prestige de l'éphémère auréole votre gloire. Votre œuvre est circonscrite en vous et rien d'elle ne vous autorise à disparaître. Que de puérils génies s'effacent au milieu du cortège de leurs œuvres! Sodoma, Mozart et Shelley reposent; mais toujours les martyrs de Sodoma s'évanouissent de béatitude sensuelle, toujours Mozart échafaude ses menuets de cristal, toujours Shelley parfume comme ces jacinthes humides et frisées qui semblent la chevelure des archanges.

Hélas vous ne danserez plus!

Je me souviens d'une terrible danse. C'était dans une arène d'Espagne. Un orchestre secouait des marches brillantes et mornes; un jeune matador, plus doré, plus aigu, plus lancinant qu'une guêpe, harcelait un taureau laqué de sang dont la noire encolure était fleurie d'une cruelle gerbe de roses trémières. Il faisait chaud. Le jeune homme très pâle, olivâtre, ayant peut-être peur, se dressait sur la pointe de ses escarpins, touchait la bête, entre les cornes, cachait son aiguillon sous la cape, dansait avec la mort.

Eh bien, lorsque je vous regarde, dispersant plus vite que les autres votre sillage de passé, brûlant votre avenir dont la cendre légère s'accumule en vous et peu à peu vous pèse, il m'apparaît qu'aussi vous dansez, en somme, avec la mort, tandis que nous nous promenons, nous nous hâtons, nous dormons sans bravoure avec elle.

JEAN COCTEAU.

196

Baron Adolphe de Meyer (1868-1946) is primarily known as an accomplished fashion photographer and society portraitist of sitters including Rita Lydig, Josephine Baker and John Barrymore. De Meyer relocated from Dresden to London in 1896, where he joined the Royal Photographic Society and the Linked Ring, a society of British Pictorialist photographers. From 1903 he corresponded with Alfred Stieglitz, eventually joining his Photo-Secession. In 1914 de Meyer became Vogue's first full-time photographer, in New York, where he remained until moving to Paris in 1921 for Harper's Bazaar. He returned to America following unrest in Europe and spent his later years in Hollywood; today de Meyer is a paragon for many contemporary fashion photographers.

This is an exacting facsimile—and first re-print overall—of Baron Adolphe de Meyer's especially rare book *Le Prélude à l'après-midi d'un faune*, first published in 1914 in a handcrafted edition of 1,000. Today only six copies are known to exist, and this Steidl edition recreates a book from Karl Lagerfeld's personal collection.

De Meyer's book is a privileged record of Vaslav Nijinsky's performance in the first ballet he choreographed: *Le Prélude à l'après-midi d'un faune* (Prelude to the Afternoon of a Faun) for Serge Diaghilev's famous Ballets Russes, set to a score by Claude Debussy and inspired by a poem by Stéphane Mallarmé. The ballet debuted in Paris in 1912 and shocked audiences and critics with its eroticism and unconventional choreography. De Meyer's 30 photos capture Nijinsky's animalistic performance as the faun surrounded by prancing nymphs, and are an important record of Léon Bakst's Symbolist sets and costumes.

In this new edition Gerhard Steidl recreates the original, published by Editions Paul Iribe & Cie, with as much attention to detail as possible. *Le Prélude* is a hand-stitched brochure with a hand-folded dust jacket. Iribe's collotypes (photomechanical ink prints) on vellum paper are recreated in offset as quadratone prints tipped-in by hand onto Somerset Cotton paper, mould-made by St Cuthbert's Mill—all in a limited edition of 1,000 books.

Photography experts regard these images as Baron de Meyer's finest work. Sergei Diaghilev valued them for another reason—as the most exceptional visual record ever made of his legendary dance company. Rita Reif, the *New York Times*

Adolphe de Meyer
Le Prélude à l'après-midi
d'un faune

Limited edition of 1,000 boxed sets

Texts by Jacques-Émile Blanche, Jean Cocteau and Auguste Rodin
100 pages
11.4 × 15 in. / 29 x 38.2 cm
30 black-and-white photographs
Quadratone
Hand-stitched brochure with tipped-in photographs housed in a box

€ 500.00 / £ 450.00 / US$ 650.00
ISBN 978-3-95829-505-6

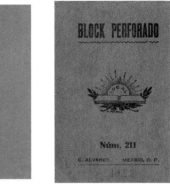

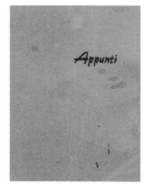

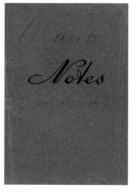

Born in 1886 in Strasbourg, the German-French artist and poet Hans/Jean Arp is one of the most important sculptors of the twentieth century. He co-founded Dada in Zurich in 1916 and later participated in Surrealist circles in Paris as well as the artists' group Abstraction-Création.

Hans / Jean Arp's diverse visual oeuvre—primarily consisting of sculptures, reliefs, drawings, collages and prints—is world-renowned, yet his sketchbooks remain relatively unknown. *Twenty Sketchbooks* seeks to remedy this by reproducing as meticulous facsimiles 20 of Arp's small sketchbooks and spiral-bound pads, made between 1950 and 1966 and today held at the Fondazione Marguerite Arp-Hagenbach, located in Arp's last atelier in Locarno, Switzerland.

This publication allows us for the first time to "hold" Arp's sketchbooks in our hands and thereby gain new insight into his working processes. Some sketches reveal themselves as drafts for fully realized artworks, yet the majority are exploratory works in themselves. *Twenty Sketchbooks* contains over 400 sketches as well as written notes by the artist. The 20 volumes, each produced at its original size, are presented in a handmade box following the design of the carton in which they were found in Arp's archive.

As I work, friendly, strange, evil, inexplicable, mute, or sleeping forms arise. Hans Arp

Co-published with the Fondazione Marguerite Arp-Hagenbach, Locarno

Hans / Jean Arp
Twenty Sketchbooks

Limited edition of 1,000 boxed sets

Edited by Rainer Hüben and Roland Scotti
Text by Rainer Hüben
4.1 x 12 x 7.1 in. / 10.5 x 30.5 x 18 cm
20 softcover books and a text booklet,
housed in an archive box
Tritone and four-color process

€ 350.00 / £ 300.00 / US$ 450.00
ISBN 978-3-95829-336-6

Vol. 1
46 pages
4.7 × 7.1 in. / 12 × 18 cm
22 color images

Vol. 2
66 pages
3.9 × 5.5 in. / 10 × 14 cm
30 color images

Vol. 3
48 pages
4.1 × 5.9 in. / 10.5 × 15 cm
19 black-and-white images

Vol. 4
66 pages
4.1 × 5.8 in. / 10.5 × 14.7 cm
31 black-and-white images

Vol. 5
56 pages
3.9 × 6 in. / 10 × 15.3 cm
27 black-and-white images

Vol. 6
54 pages
4.1 × 5.8 in. / 10.5 × 14.7 cm
25 color images

Vol. 7
66 pages
4.1 × 5.8 in. / 10.5 × 14.8 cm
29 color images

Vol. 8
54 pages
4.1 × 5.8 in. / 10.5 × 14.8 cm
22 color images

Vol. 9
52 pages
4.1 × 5.8 in. / 10.5 × 14.8 cm
18 black-and-white images

Vol. 10
82 pages
2.6 × 4.3 in. / 6.5 × 11 cm
25 black-and-white images

Vol. 11
96 pages
3 × 4.7 in. / 7.6 × 12 cm
18 color images

Vol. 12
52 pages
4.1 × 5.8 in. / 10.5 × 14.7 cm
12 black-and-white images

Vol. 13
66 pages
3.8 × 5.3 in. / 9.6 × 13.5 cm
26 color images

Vol. 14
88 pages
2.9 × 4.1 in. / 7.3 × 10.5 cm
3 color images

Vol. 15
68 pages
2.9 × 4.1 in. / 7.3 × 10.5 cm
9 color images

Vol. 16
70 pages
3.9 × 5.8 in. / 10 × 14.8 cm
33 color images

Vol. 17
80 pages
3.5 × 5.3 in. / 9 × 13.5 cm
34 color images

Vol. 18
28 pages
4.1 × 5.9 in. / 10.3 × 15.1 cm
11 black-and-white images

Vol. 19
42 pages
5.8 × 4.1 in. / 14.8 × 10.3 cm
9 black-and-white images

Vol. 20
28 pages
4.1 × 5.8 in. / 10.5 × 14.8 cm
3 black-and-white images

Text booklet in English, German, French and Italian
32 pages

Born in Duisburg in 1959, Volker Heinze is a photographer for whom the book is the primary medium; he explores his visual ideas in book form before installing his work in the gallery or museum. Heinze has published numerous monographs and his work is held in collections including Museum Folkwang in Essen, Musée d'Art moderne de la Ville de Paris and Fotomuseum Winterthur.

+ - 0 ("plus minus null") is a facsimile of a unique, handmade artist's book crafted by Volker Heinze in 1986. Its photos are the result of the young Heinze's decision to radically capture the world around him—be it cityscapes, rooms casts in warm artificial light, friends or simply objects sitting on a table. Working against the removed perspective of documentary photography, Heinze employs color not as a tool of realism but with experimental flair, and plays with focus and the inevitable "mistakes" of analogue film—all to create an original aesthetic born from the idiosyncrasies of the photographic medium.

Heinze originally presented this body of work in two forms: as the large installation *The Appearance of the Familiar*, composed of individual photos pinned to the wall in the influential 1986 exhibition "Remnants of the Authentic" at Museum Folkwang in Essen. And as + - 0—with its experimental layout, leaves of tracing paper with hand-painted quotes such as "To search for reality is like diving for pearls in an aquarium", and a booklet with excerpts from Martin Kippenberger's *241 Bildtitel zum Ausleihen*—now to be published for the first time since its inception more than 30 years ago.

At the beginning of the eighties there was a general shift towards a more subjective attitude to life and art. I found parallels to my own ideas in the music of Tom Waits and the Einstürzende Neubauten, the expressive work of a young generation of painters and the early films of Jim Jarmusch. Volker Heinze

Volker Heinze
+ - 0

Limited edition of 750 books

Texts by Florian Ebner and Martin Kippenberger
Book design by Volker Heinze
72 pages plus a 16-page text booklet
and two gatefolds
9.4 × 12.6 in. / 24 × 32 cm
36 color photographs
Four-color process
Hardcover

€ 145.00 / £ 125.00 / US$ 175.00
ISBN 978-3-95829-352-6

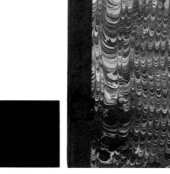

Machu Picchu steps
Peru, 1972

Afangar, Videy Island
Iceland, 1989

Basalt columns: Svartifoss
Iceland, 1989

Saqqara pyramid
Egypt, 1990

Schunnemonk Fork
Storm King Art Center, 1991

Snake Eyes and Boxcars
Geyserville, CA, 1993

Wake
2003

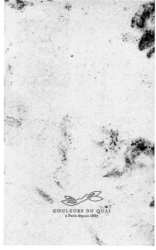

Torqued Ellipses
Guggeneheim Bilbao, Spain, 2005

Promenade
Grand Palais, Paris, 2008

East-West/West-East
Qatar, 2014

Throughout his career, the renowned American sculptor Richard Serra has kept a large number of notebooks which by now fill an entire library in his studio. Contained within them are delicate sketches of his travels, of landscapes, architecture and of other ideas, some of which the artist developed into mature sculptures and drawings. Serra has personally selected ten of his notebooks, two of which he made in Iceland in 1989 and a very recent one from Qatar, which are reproduced here in facsimile.

Richard Serra was born in San Francisco in 1938. Since the 1960s he has exhibited extensively throughout the world. In addition, Serra has created a number of site-specific sculptures in public and private venues in both North America and Europe. Serra's books at Steidl include Sculpture 1985-1998 (1999), The Matter of Time (2005), Te Tuhirangi Contour (2005), Notebooks (2011), Early Work (2014) and Vertical and Horizontal Reversals (2015). He lives in New York and Nova Scotia.

Richard Serra
Notebooks Vol. 2

Limited edition of 1,000 boxed sets
signed and numbered by Richard Serra

Machu Picchu steps, Peru, 1972
8.4 × 10.6 in. / 21.3 × 27 cm
44 pages
Leatherbound hardcover

Afangar, Videy Island, Iceland, 1989
6 × 4 in. / 14.6 × 9.4 cm
152 pages
Leatherbound hardcover

Basalt columns: Svartifoss, Iceland, 1989
10.5 × 14 in. / 25 × 33 cm
32 pages
Halfbound hardcover

Saqqara pyramid, Egypt, 1990
8.3 × 10.8 in. / 21 × 27.5 cm
44 pages
Halfbound hardcover

Schunnemonk Fork, Storm King Art Center, 1991
12.5 × 14.4 in. / 31.8 × 36.5 cm
88 pages
Clothbound hardcover

Snake Eyes and Boxcars, Geyserville, CA, 1993
8.1 × 10.6 in. / 20.6 × 27 cm
136 pages
Leatherbound hardcover

Wake, 2003
9.8 × 12.2 in. / 25 × 31 cm
48 pages
Softcover

Torqued Ellipses, Guggenheim Bilbao, Spain, 2005
12.5 × 14.4 in. / 31.8 × 36.5 cm
52 pages
Clothbound hardcover

Promenade, Grand Palais, Paris, 2008
13.8 × 8.3 in. / 35.1 × 21 cm
84 pages
Softcover

East-West/West-East, Qatar, 2014
4 × 5 in. / 9.5 × 12.5 cm
84 pages
Leatherbound

10 facsimile books housed
in a wooden crate
15.1 × 11.6 × 7.9 in. / 38.5 × 29.5 × 20 cm
764 pages total
Tritone

€ 850.00 / £ 650.00 / US$ 950.00
ISBN 978-3-86930-975-0

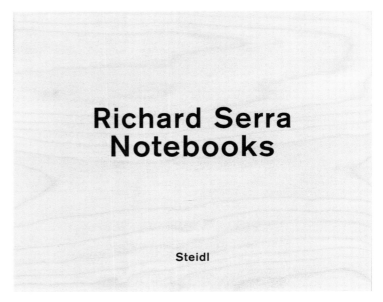

Richard Serra "Notebooks"

Vol. 1: Machu Picchu steps, Peru, 1972
Vol. 2: Afangar, Videy Island, Iceland, 1989
Vol. 3: Basalt columns: Svartifoss, Iceland, 1989
Vol. 4: Saqqara pyramid, Egypt, 1990
Vol. 5: Schunnemonk Fork, Storm King Art Center, 1991
Vol. 6: Snake Eyes and Boxcars, Geyserville, CA, 1993
Vol. 7: Wake, 2003
Vol. 8: Torqued Ellipses, Guggenheim Bilbao, Spain, 2005
Vol. 9: Promenade, Grand Palais, Paris, 2008
Vol. 10: East-West/West-East, Qatar, 2014

Facsimiles published in 2016 by Steidl Verlag, Göttingen
Printed in Germany by Gerhard Steidl

Limited edition of 1050 boxed sets
Signed and numbered by Richard Serra

Richard Serra

This set has the number
126

Edition certificate, signed and numbered by Richard Serra

**Richard Serra
Notebooks**

Steidl

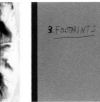

Book 1: The Phone Book (192 pages)

Book 2: The Drawing Lesson, no. 1 (48 pages)

Book 3: Footprints (48 pages)

Book 4: How Long (48 pages)

Book 5: New Mead of Poetry (32 pages)

Book 6: Clarence (16 pages)

Book 7: The Slow Motion Underneath (48 pages)

Book 8: Abstract Dreams of Printing (48 pages)

Book 9: Chalk Poems, Black & White (48 pages)

Book 10: Chalk Poems, Color (64 pages)

Book 11: Two Talks (48 pages)

Book 12: Barge (48 pages)

Book 13: Works from Nikolaistraße (96 pages)

Book 14: Oceans (second version) (80 pages)

Book 15: Batignolles (32 pages)

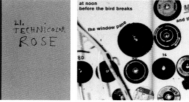

Book 16: These Europeans I knew, (a) long long time ago (48 pages)

Book 17: The Animal Fair (96 pages)

Book 18: I knew about Creeley (64 pages)

Book 19: Café de Flore (64 pages)

Book 20: Glyptotek Drawings (88 pages)

Book 21: Technicolor Rose (48 pages)

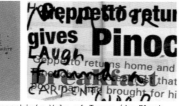

Book 22: Pinocchio's Vale of Tears (in Black and White, at random) (96 pages)

Book 23: Kaia Sand, "tiny artic ice" (32 pages)

Book 24: Personal, Personal (16 pages)

Born in 1935 in Cincinnati, Ohio, Jim
Dine completed a Bachelor of Fine Arts
at Ohio University in 1957 and has since
become one of the most profound and
prolific contemporary artists. Dine's
unparalleled career spans 60 years, and
his work is held in numerous private and
public collections. His books with Steidl
include Birds (2001), The Photographs, so
far (2003), A Printmaker's Document (2013)
and My Letter to the Troops (2017).

Jim Dine redefines everything, his life and his (he)art in these 52
books. Trying to realize the depth of his aesthetic and profane reality,
the books are also documents of an artistic consciousness, of an
intense biography, of personal likes and dislikes, of formal richness
and of exploding craftsmanship, of an exceptional imagination.
These books invent the context for a new melody for the art of Jim
Dine, for all the major byways of this seemingly inexhaustible creativity, which combines dream and reality — it is a composition for all the
people who would like to sing a new song, maybe their own song.
Dine has reflected authentically on his own identity and through it the
identity of reality, nature, art, thoughts, feelings in an extraordinary
poetic way: we see a POEM, we read an IMAGE.
They are books one may read and regard as a summary of an unusual life.

This Hot Dream *first appeared as an idea 13 years ago. Steidl*
embraced and blessed the project so I went ahead. I stewed about
it for two years then I stood around waiting to talk to Gerhard about
it then finally I got down to putting the books together. My method,
as in all my work, is the use of collage, painting and drawing, and
correcting; coupled with my writing and my untouched photographs.
The fact of making a book a week and the sensual possibilities i.e. the
act of making a union with humans through the smell of the ink on the
paper, the feel of the images and words. Hot Dream *tells a lot about*
me, Dine, and bookmaking.

Jim Dine, Göttingen, June 2018

Jim Dine
Hot Dream (52 Books)

Limited edition of 500 boxed sets

Textbook by Roland Scotti
Book design by Jim Dine, Gerhard Steidl
and Jonas Wettre
6.5 x 8.9 in. / 16.5 x 22.7 cm
52 softcovers and an illustrated bilingual
textbook (German/English) housed in a box
Tritone and four-color process

€ 150.00 / £ 135.00 / US$ 180.00
ISBN 978-3-86930-132-7

Illustrated textbook

Boxed set closed

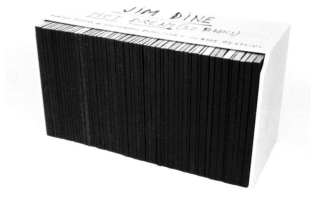

Boxed set open

Book 25: Mary (96 pages)

Book 26: A History of France (112 pages)

Book 27: Drawings from life (48 pages)

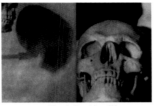

Book 28: Face never seen, Head in the Mirror (64 pages)

Book 29: Pastoral poem of Revenge (32 pages)

Book 30: Kaia Sand, lotto (32 pages)

Book 31: Witnesses (48 pages)

Book 32: The Drawing Lesson, no.2 (24 pages)

Book 33: Santa Hell (96 pages)

Book 34: The Flowering Sheets (22 pages)

Book 35: Swedish and Northwest Plants and Flowers (32 pages)

Book 36: The Woodburner Alphabet (64 pages)

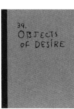

Book 37: Images of the Boy (128 pages)

Book 38: Some Poems (64 pages)

Book 39: Objects of Desire (64 pages)

Book 40: Hardtalk (48 pages)

Book 41: Dark Movie (32 pages)

Book 42: Further Adventures of Mr and Mrs Jim and Ron (128 pages)

Book 43: Swimming Laps (32 pages)

Book 44: Cottonwood Days and Night (160 pages)

Book 45: Jesus Walking (64 pages)

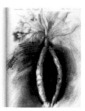

Book 46: Time Machine in Blue (112 pages)

Book 47: Some Greeks, Some Romans. 1993-1996 (160 pages)

Book 48: Ode to Sad (16 pages)

Book 49: Bluebook, Recollection of
Wittgenstein (112 pages)

Book 50: Entrada Drive, 2nd version (128 pages)

Book 51: Love in the Everglades (128 pages)

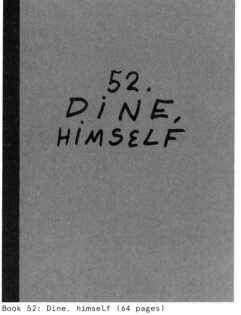

Book 52: Dine, himself (64 pages)

JIM DINE HOT DREAM

(52 BOOKS)

Jim Dine redefines everything, his life and his (he)art in these 52 books

Backlist

Abbott, Berenice
The Unknown Berenice Abbott

€ 285.00 / £ 240.00 / US$ 350.00
ISBN 978-3-86930-650-6

Adams, Bryan
Untitled

€ 125.00 / £ 95.00 / US$ 125.00
ISBN 978-3-86930-988-0

Abbott, Berenice
Paris Portraits 1925-1930

€ 75.00 / £ 70.00 / US$ 85.00
ISBN 978-3-86930-314-7

Adams, Bryan
Exposed

€ 68.00 / £ 60.00 / US$ 75.00
ISBN 978-3-86930-500-4

A-chan
Off Beat

€ 20.00 / £ 16.00 / US$ 25.00
ISBN 978-3-86930-416-8

Adams, Bryan
Homeless

€ 38.00 / £ 35.00 / US$ 45.00
ISBN 978-3-95829-387-8

A-chan
Vibrant Home

€ 20.00 / £ 16.00 / US$ 25.00
ISBN 978-3-86930-415-1

Adams, Robert
Gone?

€ 48.00 / £ 45.00 / US$ 55.00
ISBN 978-3-86521-917-6

A-chan
Salt'n Vinegar

€ 40.00 / £ 35.00 / US$ 50.00
ISBN 978-3-86930-784-8

Adams, Robert
Tree Line

€ 35.00 / £ 30.00 / US$ 40.00
ISBN 978-3-86521-956-5

Adams, Bryan
Wounded. The Legacy of War

€ 58.00 / £ 48.00 / US$ 65.00
ISBN 978-3-86930-677-3

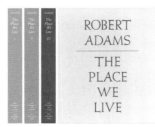

Adams, Robert
The Place We Live

€ 175.00 / £ 165.00 / US$ 200.00
ISBN 978-3-86930-533-2

Adams, Robert
The New West

€ 35.00 / £ 28.00 / US$ 40.00
ISBN 978-3-86930-900-2

Bailey, David
Bailey's East End

€ 98.00 / £ 90.00 / US$ 125.00
ISBN 978-3-86930-534-9

Adams, Robert
Cottonwoods

€ 45.00 / £ 38.00 / US$ 50.00
ISBN 978-3-95829-096-9

Bailey, David
Bailey's Democracy

€ 45.00 / £ 40.00 / US$ 50.00
ISBN 978-3-86521-192-7

Adams, Robert
Our Lives and Our Children

€ 48.00 / £ 40.00 / US$ 55.00
ISBN 978-3-95829-097-6

Bailey, David
Havana

€ 45.00 / £ 40.00 / US$ 50.00
ISBN 978-3-86521-270-2

Adams, Robert
Perfect Places, Perfect Company

€ 80.00 / £ 68.00 / US$ 85.00
ISBN 978-3-95829-169-0

Bailey, David
Is That So Kid

€ 45.00 / £ 40.00 / US$ 50.00
ISBN 978-3-86521-632-8

Adams, Robert
From the Missouri West

€ 95.00 / £ 85.00 / US$ 125.00
ISBN 978-3-95829-168-3

Bailey, David
NY JS DB 62

€ 45.00 / £ 40.00 / US$ 50.00
ISBN 978-3-86521-414-0

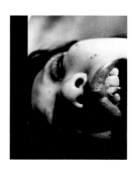

Araki, Nobuyoshi
Impossible Love

€ 58.00 / £ 58.00 / US$ 65.00
ISBN 978-3-95829-553-7

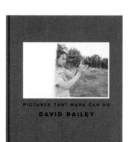

Bailey, David
Pictures that Mark can do

€ 45.00 / £ 40.00 / US$ 50.00
ISBN 978-3-86521-367-9

Bailey, David
8 Minutes

€ 45.00 / £ 40.00 / US$ 50.00
ISBN 978-3-86521-864-3

Balthus
The Last Studies

€ 480.00 / £ 440.00 / US$ 550.00
ISBN 978-3-86930-685-8

Bailey, David
Flowers, Skulls, Contacts

€ 45.00 / £ 40.00 / US$ 50.00
ISBN 978-3-86930-128-0

Baltz, Lewis
Works – Last Edition

€ 950.00
ISBN 978-3-95829-132-4

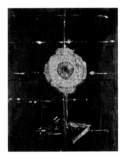

Bailey, David
Eye

€ 45.00 / £ 40.00 / US$ 50.00
ISBN 978-3-86521-708-0

Baltz, Lewis
Rule Without Exception /
Only Exceptions

€ 65.00 / £ 50.00 / US$ 80.00
ISBN 978-3-86930-110-5

Bailey, David
Delhi Dilemma

€ 98.00 / £ 90.00 / US$ 125.00
ISBN 978-3-86521-991-6

Baltz, Lewis
Common Objects

€ 40.00 / £ 30.00 / US$ 50.00
ISBN 978-3-86930-785-5

Bailey, David
Tears and Tears

€ 45.00 / £ 40.00 / US$ 50.00
ISBN 978-3-86930-989-7

Baltz, Lewis
Texts

€ 24.00 / £ 20.00 / US$ 30.00
ISBN 978-3-86930-436-6

Bailey, David
Bailey´s Naga Hills

€ 45.00 / £ 40.00 / US$ 50.00
ISBN 978-3-95829-170-6

Baltz, Lewis
Candlestick Point

€ 75.00 / £ 70.00 / US$ 85.00
ISBN 978-3-86930-109-9

Baltz, Lewis
Venezia Marghera

€ 8,900.00 / £ 7,900.00 /
US$ 10,000.00
ISBN 978-3-86930-313-0

Lewis Baltz

€ 70.00 / £ 60.00 / US$ 80.00
ISBN 978-3-95829-279-6

Banier, François-Marie
Imprudences

€ 38.00 / £ 32.00 / US$ 45.00
ISBN 978-3-86930-919-4

Banier, François-Marie
Never Stop Dancing

€ 10.00 / £ 8.00 / US$ 12.00
ISBN 978-3-86930-577-6

Baumann / Chuang / Onabanjo (eds.)
Recent Histories

€ 65.00 / £ 60.00 / US$ 75.00
ISBN 978-3-95829-350-2

Berndt, Jerry
Beautiful America

€ 38.00 / £ 30.00 / US$ 45.00
ISBN 978-3-86930-898-2

Beuys, Joseph / Staeck, Klaus
Honey is flowing in all directions

€ 35.00 / £ 30.00 / US$ 40.00
ISBN 978-3-88243-538-2

Blumenfeld, Erwin
Blumenfeld Studio

€ 34.00 / £ 28.00 / US$ 40.00
ISBN 978-3-86930-531-8

Bolofo, Koto
Große Komplikation /
Grand Complication

€ 98.00 / £ 89.00 / US$ 100.00
ISBN 978-3-86930-055-9

Bolofo, Koto
Lord Snowdon

€ 75.00 / £ 68.00 / US$ 85.00
ISBN 978-3-86930-329-1

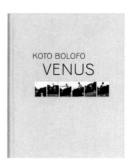

Bolofo, Koto
Venus Williams

€ 45.00 / £ 35.00 / US$ 55.00
ISBN 978-3-86521-602-1

Bolofo, Koto
Vroom! Vroom!

€ 45.00 / £ 35.00 / US$ 55.00
ISBN 978-3-86521-961-9

Bourdin, Guy
A Message For You

€ 55.00 / £ 50.00 / US$ 65.00
ISBN 978-3-86930-551-6

Bourdin, Guy
Untouched

€ 55.00 / £ 50.00 / US$ 65.00
ISBN 978-3-86930-934-7

Burri, René
Mouvement

€ 85.00 / £ 75.00 / US$ 95.00
ISBN 978-3-86930-820-3

Burtynsky, Edward
Oil

€ 98.00 / £ 85.00 / US$ 125.00
ISBN 978-3-86521-943-5

Burtynsky, Edward
Salt Pans
Little Rann of Kutch, Gujarat,
India

€ 65.00 / £ 60.00 / US$ 75.00
ISBN 978-3-95829-240-6

Burtynsky, Edward
Anthropocene

€ 95.00 / £ 90.00 / US$ 125.00
ISBN 978-3-95829-489-9

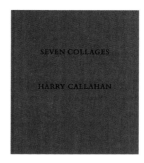

Callahan, Harry
Seven Collages

€ 28.00 / £ 22.00 / US$ 40.00
ISBN 978-3-86930-140-2

Campany, David (ed.)
Walker Evans: the magazine work

€ 58.00 / £ 50.00 / US$ 65.00
ISBN 978-3-86930-259-1

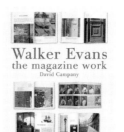

Cartier-Bresson, Henri
The Decisive Moment

€ 98.00 / £ 78.00 / US$ 125.00
ISBN 978-3-86930-788-6

Chan, Theseus (ed.)
Steidl-Werk No. 23:
Masaho Anotani, Deformed

€ 48.00 / £ 40.00 / US$ 55.00
ISBN 978-3-95829-120-1

Clay, Maude Schuyler
Mississippi History

€ 65.00 / £ 58.00 / US$ 75.00
ISBN 978-3-86930-974-3

Clay, Langdon
Cars – New York City, 1974–1976

€ 95.00 / £ 90.00 / US$ 125.00
ISBN 978-3-95829-171-3

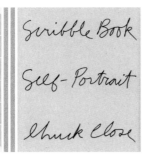

Close, Chuck
Scribble Book: Self-Portrait

€ 125.00 / £ 100.00 / US$ 145.00
ISBN 978-3-86521-492-8

Comte, Michel
Light

€ 98.00 / £ 85.00 / US$ 125.00
ISBN 978-3-95829-119-5

Cohen, John
Here and Gone

€ 38.00 / £ 32.00 / US$ 48.00
ISBN 978-3-86930-604-9

Courtney-Clarke, Margaret
Cry Sadness into the Coming Rain

€ 75.00 / £ 70.00 / US$ 80.00
ISBN 978-3-95829-253-6

Cohen, John
The High & Lonesome Sound

€ 45.00 / £ 35.00 / US$ 50.00
ISBN 978-3-86930-254-6

D'Agati, Mauro
Alamar

€ 45.00 / £ 35.00 / US$ 50.00
ISBN 978-3-86521-954-1

Cohen, John
Cheap rents ... and de Kooning

€ 24.00 / £ 20.00 / US$ 25.00
ISBN 978-3-86930-903-3

D'Agati, Mauro
Sit Lux et Lux Fuit

€ 48.00 / £ 38.00 / US$ 50.00
ISBN ISBN 978-3-86930-488-5

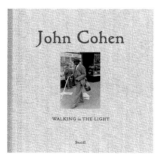

Cohen, John
Walking in the Light

€ 38.00 / £ 30.00 / US$ 45.00
ISBN 978-3-86930-772-5

D'Agati, Mauro
Palermo Unsung

€ 45.00 / £ 39.50 / US$ 50.00
ISBN 978-3-86521-918-3

Cole, Teju / Sheikh, Fazal
Human Archipelago

€ 40.00 / £ 35.00 / US$ 45.00
ISBN 978-3-95829-568-1

D'Agati, Mauro
Marzia's Family

€ 40.00 / £ 34.00 / US$ 45.00
ISBN 978-3-86930-605-6

Das, Kapil
Something So Clear

€ 35.00 / £ 30.00 / US$ 40.00
ISBN 978-3-95829-318-2

d'Urso, Alessandra /
Borghese, Alessandra
For Friends

€ 95.00 / £ 80.00 / US$ 95.00
ISBN 978-3-95829-133-1

d'Urso, Alessandra /
Borghese, Alessandra
Jubileum

€ 28.00 / £ 25.00 / US$ 30.00
ISBN 978-3-95829-258-1

Moyra Davey

€ 48.00 / £ 40.00 / US$ 55.00
ISBN 978-3-95829-567-4

Davidson, Anna Mia
Cuba Black and White

€ 48.00 / £ 40.00 / US$ 60.00
ISBN 978-3-95829-028-0

Davidson, Bruce
In Color

€ 78.00 / £ 68.00 / US$ 85.00
ISBN 978-3-86930-564-6

Davidson, Bruce
Subway

€ 58.00 / £ 52.00
ISBN 978-3-86930-294-2

Davidson, Bruce
Black & White

€ 300.00 / £ 280.00 / US$ 350.00
ISBN 978-3-86930-432-8

Davidson, Bruce
England / Scotland 1960

€ 45.00 / £ 40.00 / US$ 50.00
ISBN 978-3-86930-486-1

Davidson, Bruce
Outside Inside

€ 300.00 / £ 280.00 / US$ 350.00
ISBN 978-3-86521-908-4

Davidson, Bruce
Nature of Los Angeles
2008-2013

€ 38.00 / £ 30.00 / US$ 45.00
ISBN 978-3-86930-814-2

De Pietri, Paola
Istanbul New Stories

€ 75.00 / £ 70.00 / US$ 85.00
ISBN 978-3-95829-110-2

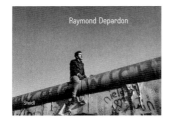

Depardon, Raymond
Berlin

€ 35.00 / £ 30.00 / US$ 40.00
ISBN 978-3-86930-790-9

Diépois, Aline / Gizolme, Thomas
Abstrakt Zermatt

€ 40.00 / £ 35.00 / US$ 45.00
ISBN 978-3-86930-580-6

Dine, Jim
My Tools

€ 28.00 / £ 20.00 / US$ 35.00
ISBN 978-3-86930-828-9

Dine, Jim
Birds

€ 50.00 / £ 45.00 / US$ 55.00
ISBN 978-3-88243-240-4

Dine, Jim
Entrada Drive

€ 50.00 / £ 45.00 / US$ 55.00
ISBN 978-3-86521-080-7

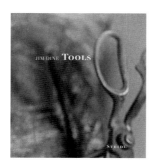

Dine, Jim
Tools

€ 50.00 / £ 45.00 / US$ 55.00
ISBN 978-3-86930-647-6

Dine, Jim
The Photographs,
So Far (vols. 1-4)

€ 150.00 / £ 125.00 / US$ 180.00
ISBN 978-3-88243-905-2

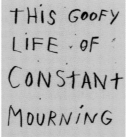

Dine, Jim
This Goofy Life of Constant
Mourning

€ 48.00 / £ 40.00 / US$ 55.00
ISBN 978-3-88243-967-0

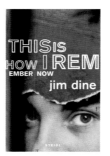

Dine, Jim
This Is How I Remember Now

€ 48.00 / £ 33.00 / US$ 50.00
ISBN 978-3-86521-603-8

Dine, Jim
Hello Yellow Glove

€ 28.00 / £ 20.00 / US$ 35.00
ISBN 978-3-86930-484-7

Dine, Jim
A Printmaker's Document

€ 30.00 / £ 25.00 / US$ 40.00
ISBN 978-3-86930-644-5

Dine, Jim
Paris Reconnaissance

€ 35.00 / £ 30.00 / US$ 45.00
ISBN 978-3-95829-388-5

Dine, Jim
Jewish Fate

€ 18.00 / £ 15.00 / US$ 20.00
ISBN 978-3-95829-322-9

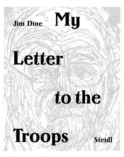

Dine, Jim
My Letter to the Troops

€ 18.00 / £ 15.00 / US$ 20.00
ISBN 978-3-95829-339-7

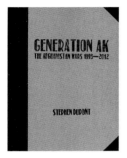

Dupont, Stephen
Generation AK

€ 78.00 / £ 70.00 / US$ 85.00
ISBN 978-3-86930-727-5

Eggleston, William
From Black and White to Color

€ 38.00 / £ 32.00 / US$ 45.00
ISBN 978-3-86930-793-0

Eggleston, William
Los Alamos revisited

€ 350.00 / £ 300.00 / US$ 400.00
ISBN 978-3-86930-532-5

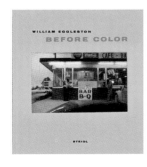

Eggleston, William
Before Color

€ 48.00 / £ 40.00 / US$ 55.00
ISBN 978-3-86930-122-8

Eggleston, William
At Zenith

€ 48.00 / £ 40.00 / US$ 55.00
ISBN 978-3-86930-710-7

Eggleston, William
The Democratic Forest

€ 650.00 / £ 600.00 / US$ 750.00
ISBN 978-3-86930-792-3

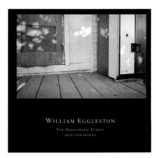

Eggleston, William
The Democratic Forest
Selected Works

€ 45.00 / £ 38.00
ISBN 978-3-95829-256-7
[Distributed in the USA by David
Zwirner (D.A.P.)]

William Eggleston
Election Eve

€ 80,00 / £ 75,00 / US$ 85,00
ISBN 978-3-95829-266-6

Elgort, Arthur
The Big Picture

€ 78.00 / £ 68.00 / US$ 85.00
ISBN 978-3-86930-543-1

Ehrlich, Richard
Face the Music

€ 50.00 / £ 45.00 / US$ 55.00
ISBN 978-3-86930-966-8

Epstein, Mitch
Berlin

€ 45.00 / £ 40.00 / US$ 55.00
ISBN 978-3-86930-224-9

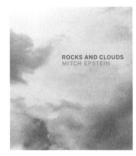

Epstein, Mitch
American Power

€ 65.00 / £ 60.00 / US$ 75.00
ISBN 978-3-86521-924-4

Epstein, Mitch
Rocks and Clouds

€ 65.00 / £ 58.00 / US$ 75.00
ISBN 978-3-95829-160-7

Eskildsen, Joakim
American Realities

€ 32.00 / £ 28.00 / US$ 40.00
ISBN 978-3-86930-734-3

Faurer, Louis
Louis Faurer

€ 34.00 / £ 29,80 / US$ 40.00
ISBN 978-3-95829-247-5

Fernandes, Walter / Hurst, Miguel
Angola Cinemas

€ 45.00 / £ 40.00 / US$ 55.00
ISBN 978-3-86930-794-7

Ferrez, Marc / Polidori, Robert
Rio

€ 125.00 / £ 110.00 / US$ 150.00
ISBN 978-3-86930-910-1

Frank, Robert
The Americans

€ 35.00 / £ 30.00 / US$ 40.00
ISBN 978-3-86521-584-0

Frank, Robert
Looking In: Robert Frank's The
Americans – Expanded Edition

€ 85.00 / £ 75.00 / US$ 95.00
ISBN 978-3-86521-806-3

Frank, Robert
Come Again

€ 35.00 / £ 30.00 / US$ 40.00
ISBN 978-3-86521-261-0

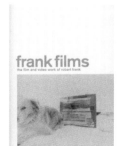

Frank, Robert
Frank Films

€ 45.00 / £ 40.00 / US$ 50.00
ISBN 978-3-86521-815-5

Frank, Henry
Father Photographer

€ 24.00 / £ 20.00 / US$ 25.00
ISBN 978-3-86521-814-8

ROBERT FRANK
FILM WORKS

STEIDL

Frank, Robert
Film Works

€ 150.00 / £ 120.00 / US$ 175.00
ISBN 978-3-95829-036-5

ONE HOUR
Robert Frank

Frank, Robert
One Hour

€ 10.00 / £ 8.00 / US$ 12.00
ISBN 978-3-86521-364-8

Frank, Robert
HOLD STILL – keep going

€ 40.00 / £ 35.00 / US$ 45.00
ISBN 978-3-86930-904-0

Robert Frank PANGNIRTUNG

Frank, Robert
Pangnirtung

€ 35.00 / £ 30.00 / US$ 40.00
ISBN 978-3-86930-198-3

Frank, Robert
Household Inventory Record

€ 30.00 / £ 25.00 / US$ 35.00
ISBN 978-3-86930-660-5

ROBERT FRANK PARIS

Frank, Robert
Paris

€ 35.00 / £ 30.00 / US$ 40.00
ISBN 978-3-86521-524-6

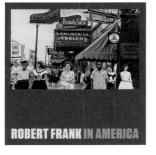
ROBERT FRANK IN AMERICA

Frank, Robert
In America

€ 45.00 / £ 40.00 / US$ 50.00
ISBN 978-3-86930-735-0

PARK/SLEEP
ROBERT FRANK

Frank, Robert
Park/Sleep

€ 27.00 / £ 24.00 / US$ 30.00
ISBN 978-3-86930-585-1

ME AND MY BROTHER

Frank, Robert
Me and My Brother

€ 38.00 / £ 34.00 / US$ 45.00
ISBN 978-3-86521-363-1

PARTIDA
ROBERT FRANK

Frank, Robert
Partida

€ 27.00 / £ 24.00 / US$ 30.00
ISBN 978-3-86930-795-4

ROBERT FRANK
New York to Nova Scotia

Frank, Robert
New York to Nova Scotia

€ 35.00 / £ 30.00 / US$ 40.00
ISBN 978-3-86521-013-5

PERU

Photographs by ROBERT FRANK

Frank, Robert
Peru

€ 30.00 / £ 25.00 / US$ 35.00
ISBN 978-3-86521-692-2

Frank, Robert
Pull My Daisy

€ 10.00 / £ 8.00 / US$ 12.00
ISBN 978-3-86521-673-1

Frank, Robert
Leon of Juda

€ 27.00 / £ 24.00 / US$ 30.00
ISBN 978-3-95829-311-3

Frank, Robert
Tal Uf Tal Ab

€ 27.00 / £ 24.00 / US$ 30.00
ISBN 978-3-86930-101-3

Frank, Robert
The Lines of My Hand

€ 30.00 / £ 28.00 / US$ 35.00
ISBN 978-3-95829-320-5

Frank, Robert
Valencia

€ 35.00 / £ 30.00 / US$ 40.00
ISBN 978-3-86930-502-8

Frank, Robert
London/Wales

€ 38.00 / £ 34.00 / US$ 45.00
ISBN 978-3-86521-362-4

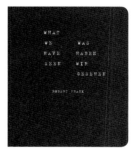

Frank, Robert
Was haben wir gesehen /
What we have seen

€ 27.00 / £ 24.00 / US$ 30.00
ISBN 978-3-95829-095-2

Frank, Robert
Good days quiet

€ 35.00 / £ 30.00 / US$ 40.00
ISBN 978-3-95829-550-6

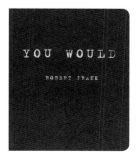

Frank, Robert
You Would

€ 27.00 / £ 24.00 / US$ 30.00
ISBN 978-3-86930-418-2

Freund, David
Gas Stop

€ 98.00 / £ 89.00 / US$ 125.00
ISBN 978-3-95829-173-7

Frank, Robert
Zero Mostel Reads a Book

€ 15.00 / £ 10.00 / US$ 18.00
ISBN 978-3-86521-586-4

Friedlander, Lee
Chain Link

€ 38.00 / £ 34.00 / US$ 40.00
ISBN 978-3-95829-259-8

Gohlke, Frank / Sternfeld, Joel
Landscape as Longing: Queens,
New York

€ 75.00 / £ 70.00 / US$ 85.00
ISBN 978-3-95829-032-7

Goldblatt, David
The Transported of Kwandebele

€ 65.00 / £ 48.00 / US$ 80.00
ISBN 978-3-86930-586-8

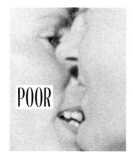

Goldberg, Jim
Rich and Poor

€ 75.00 / £ 65.00 / US$ 95.00
ISBN 978-3-86930-688-9

Goldblatt, David
Structures of Dominion
and Democracy

€ 48.00 / £ 45.00 / US$ 65.00
ISBN 978-3-95829-391-5

Goldblatt, David
In Boksburg

€ 45.00 / £ 38.00 / US$ 50.00
ISBN 978-3-86930-796-1

Goldin, Nan
Diving For Pearls

€ 35.00 / £ 30.00 / US$ 40.00
ISBN 978-3-95829-094-5

Goldblatt, David
On the Mines

€ 58.00 / £ 48.00 / US$ 65.00
ISBN 978-3-86930-491-5

Goldin, Nan
The Beautiful Smile

€ 45.00 / £ 40.00 / US$ 55.00
ISBN 978-3-95829-174-4

Goldblatt, David
Particulars

€ 58.00 / £ 42.00 / US$ 70.00
ISBN 978-3-86930-777-0

Felix Gonzalez-Torres

€ 58.00 / £ 48.00 / US$ 65.00
ISBN 978-3-86930-921-7

Goldblatt, David
Regarding Intersections

€ 68.00 / £ 58.00 / US$ 75.00
ISBN 978-3-86930-714-5

Gossage, John
The Thirty-Two Inch Ruler /
Map of Babylon

€ 58.00 / £ 52.00 / US$ 60.00
ISBN 978-3-86521-710-3

Gossage, John
Looking up Ben James - A Fable

€ 65.00 / £ 60.00 / US$ 75.00
ISBN 978-3-86930-589-9

Grossman, Sid
The Life and Work of Sid Grossman

€ 48.00 / £ 45.00 / US$ 55.00
ISBN 978-3-95829-125-6

Grätz, Roland / Neubauer,
Hans-Joachim (eds.)
Human Rights Watch
Ed Kashi

€ 30.00 / £ 24.00 / US$ 35.00
ISBN 978-3-95829-167-6

Gudzowaty, Tomasz
Beyond the Body

€ 38.00 / £ 32.00 / US$ 45.00
ISBN 978-3-95829-040-2

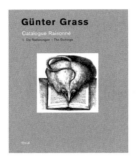

Grass, Günter
Catalogue Raisonné 1
The Etchings

€ 98.00 / £ 90.00 / US$ 125.00
ISBN 978-3-86521-565-9

Gudzowaty, Tomasz
Photography as a New Kind of
Love Poem

€ 78.00 / £ 65.00 / US$ 85.00
ISBN 978-3-95829-041-9

Grass, Günter
Catalogue Raisonné 2
The Lithographs

€ 98.00 / £ 90.00 / US$ 125.00
ISBN 978-3-86521-566-6

Gudzowaty, Tomasz
Closer

€ 88.00 / £ 78.00 / US$ 95.00
ISBN 978-3-95829-044-0

Angela Grauerholz

€ 58.00 / £ 48.00 / US$ 65.00
ISBN 978-3-95829-122-5

Gudzowaty, Tomasz
Proof

€ 30.00 / £ 25.00 / US$ 35.00
ISBN 978-3-95829-164-5

Howard Greenberg Collection

€ 38.00 / £ 32.00 / US$ 45.00
ISBN 978-3-86930-736-7

Gundlach, F.C.
The Photographic Work

€ 75.00 / £ 70.00 / US$ 85.00
ISBN 978-3-86521-594-9

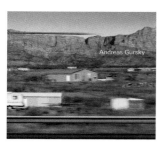

Andreas Gursky

€ 50.00 / US$ 60.00
ISBN 978-3-95829-392-2
[Distributed in the UK by
Cornerhouse Publications]

Hechenblaikner, Lois
Volksmusik

€ 38.00 / £ 35.00 / US$ 40.00
ISBN 978-3-95829-175-1

Haas, Ernst
On Set

€ 58.00 / £ 48.00 / US$ 70.00
ISBN 978-3-86930-587-5

Heiting, Manfred (ed.)
Czech and Slovak Photo
Publications, 1918-1989

€ 125.00 / £ 98.00 / US$ 145.00
ISBN 978-3-95829-497-4

Hanzlova, Jitka
Cotton Rose

€ 35.00 / £ 30.00 / US$ 40.00
ISBN 978-3-86930-127-3

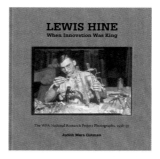

Hine, Lewis
When Innovation Was King

€ 40.00 / £ 38.00 / US$ 45.00
ISBN 978-3-95829-189-8

Harris, Susan and Staniszewski,
Mary Anne (eds.)
Exit Art

€ 50.00 / £ 40.00 / US$ 55.00
ISBN 978-3-95829-197-3

Hofer, Evelyn
New York

€ 45.00 / £ 40.00 / US$ 50.00
ISBN 978-3-95829-348-9

Heath, Dave
Dialogues with Solitudes

€ 40.00 / £ 35.00 / US$ 50.00
ISBN 978-3-95829-543-8

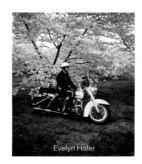

Hofer, Evelyn
Begegnungen/Encounters

€ 58.00 / £ 55.00 / US$ 65.00
ISBN 978-3-95829-563-6

Hechenblaikner, Lois
Winter Wonderland

€ 38.00 / £ 30.00 / US$ 40.00
ISBN 978-3-86930-284-3

Hoppé, E. O.
The German Work

€ 58.00 / £ 48.00 / US$ 65.00
ISBN 978-3-86930-937-8

Horn, Roni
Another Water

€ 38.00 / £ 35.00 / US$ 45.00
ISBN 978-3-86930-318-5

Horn, Roni
bird

€ 38.00 / £ 35.00 / US$ 45.00
ISBN 978-3-86521-669-4

Horn, Roni
Haraldsdóttir, Part Two

€ 85.00 / £ 70.00 / US$ 95.00
ISBN 978-3-86930-317-8

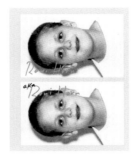

Horn, Roni
Roni Horn aka Roni Horn

€ 50.00 / £ 45.00 / US$ 60.00
ISBN 978-3-86521-831-5

Horn, Roni
Cabinet of

€ 65.00 / £ 55.00 / US$ 75.00
ISBN 978-3-88243-864-2

Horn, Roni
Herdubreid at Home

€ 20.00 / £ 13.00 / US$ 20.00
ISBN 978-3-86521-457-7

Horn, Roni
Her, Her, Her, & Her

€ 35.00 / £ 24.00 / US$ 40.00
ISBN 978-3-86521-035-7

Horn, Roni
AKA

€ 38.00 / £ 35.00 / US$ 45.00
ISBN 978-3-86930-133-4

Horn, Roni
Index Cixous

€ 22.50 / £ 15.00 / US$ 20.00
ISBN 978-3-86521-135-4

Horn, Roni
Hack Wit

€ 38.00 / £ 35.00 / US$ 45.00
ISBN 97-3-86930-982-8

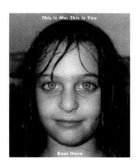

Horn, Roni
This is Me, This is You

€ 28.00 / £ 25.00 / US$ 30.00
ISBN 978-3-88243-798-0

Horn, Roni
The Selected Gifts, 1974-2015

€ 38.00 / £ 35.00 / US$ 45.00
ISBN 978-3-95829-162-1

Horn, Roni
Th Rose Prblm

€ 38.00 / £ 35.00 / US$ 45.00
ISBN 978-3-95829-271-0

Horn, Roni
Dogs' Chorus

€ 50.00 / £ 45.00 / US$ 60.00
ISBN 978-3-95829-536-0

Horn, Roni
Remembered Words
A Specimen Concordance

€ 18.00 / £ 15.00 / US$ 25.00
ISBN 978-3-95829-564-3

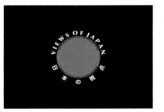

Huyck, Willard / Katz, Gloria
Views of Japan

€ 80.00 / £ 75.00 / US$ 85.00
ISBN 978-3-95829-177-5

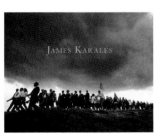

James Karales

€ 58.00 / £ 45.00 / US$ 64.00
ISBN 978-3-86930-444-1

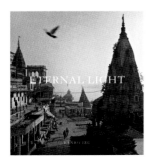

Izu, Kenro
Eternal Light

€ 40.00 / £ 38.00 / US$ 45.00
ISBN 978-3-95829-190-4

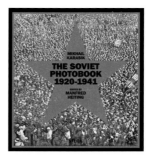

Karasik, Mikhail
The Soviet Photobook

€ 125.00 / £ 98.00 / US$ 150.00
ISBN 978-3-95829-031-0

Karel, Betsy
America's Stage: Times Square

€ 40.00 / £ 35.00 / US$ 45.00
ISBN 978-3-95829-227-7

Keel, Philipp
Splash

€ 48.00 / £ 38.00 / US$ 65.00
ISBN 978-3-86930-799-2

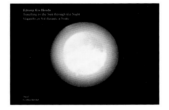

Kia Henda, Kiluanji
Travelling to the Sun through the Night

€ 40.00 / £ 35.00 / US$ 45.00
ISBN 978-3-86930-800-5

Killip, Chris
In Flagrante Two

€ 65.00 / £ 58.00 / US$ 75.00
ISBN 978-3-86930-960-6

Killip, Chris
Seacoal

€ 48.00 / £ 38.00 / US$ 60.00
ISBN 978-3-86930-256-0

Killip, Chris
Pirelli Work

€ 45.00 / £ 38.00 / US$ 50.00
ISBN 978-3-86930-961-3

Kuhn, Mona
She Disappeared into
Complete Silence

€ 45,00 / £ 40.00 / US$ 50.00
ISBN 978-3-95829-180-5

Killip, Chris
Isle of Man Revisited

€ 48.00 / £ 40.00 / US$ 60.00
ISBN 978-3-86930-959-0

Lagerfeld, Karl
Byzantine Fragments

€ 125.00 / £ 100.00 / US$ 140.00
ISBN 978-3-86930-246-1

Kosorukov, Gleb
Heroes of Labour

€ 58.00 / £ 54.00 / US$ 65.00
ISBN 978-3-86930-689-6

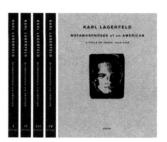

Lagerfeld, Karl
Metamorphoses of an American

€ 98.00 / £ 80.00 / US$ 110.00
ISBN 978-3-86521-522-2

Kuhn, Mona
Bordeaux Series

€ 58.00 / £ 50.00 / US$ 65.00
ISBN 978-3-86930-308-6

Lagerfeld, Karl
The Glory of Water

€ 200.00 / £ 170.00 / US$ 220.00
ISBN 978-3-86930-708-4

Kuhn, Mona
Evidence

€ 40.00 / £ 35.00 / US$ 45.00
ISBN 978-3-86521-372-3

Lagerfeld, Karl
Casa Malaparte

€ 70.00 / £ 60.00 / US$ 80.00
ISBN 978-3-95829-033-4

Kuhn, Mona
Photographs

€ 40.00 / £ 35.00 / US$ 45.00
ISBN 978-3-86521-008-1

Lagerfeld, Karl
Villa Noailles
Hyères - Été 1995

€ 48.00 / £ 40.00 / US$ 60.00
ISBN 978-3-95829-037-2

Lagerfeld, Karl / Djian, Babeth
Numéro Couture by Karl Lagerfeld

€ 85.00 / £ 75.00 / US$ 95.00
ISBN 978-3-95829-057-0

Lebeck, Robert
1968

€ 45.00 / £ 40.00 / US$ 50.00
ISBN 978-3-95829-419-6

Lagerfeld, Karl
Paris Photo

€ 40.00 / £ 35.00 / US$ 45.00
ISBN 978-3-95829-354-0

Leiter, Saul
Early Black and White

€ 68.00 / £ 58.00 / US$ 75.00
ISBN 978-3-86521-413-3

Lake, Suzy

€ 58.00 / £ 48.00 / US$ 65.00
ISBN 978-3-95829-282-6

Leiter, Saul
Early Color

€ 38.00 / £ 32,00 / US$ 45.00
ISBN 978-3-86521-139-2

Laval, Karine
Poolscapes

€ 38.00 / £ 35.00 / US$ 45.00
ISBN 978-3-95829-261-1

Leiter, Saul
In My Room

€ 38.00 / £ 32.00 / US$ 45.00
ISBN 978-3-95829-103-4

Leaf, June
Record 1974/75

€ 40.00 / £ 35.00 / US$ 45.00
ISBN 978-3-86930-045-0

Leutwyler, Henry
Ballet

€ 65.00 / £ 55.00 / US$ 75.00
ISBN 978-3-86930-906-4

Leaf, June
Thought is Infinite

€ 35.00 / £ 28.00 / US$ 40.00
ISBN 978-3-95829-102-7

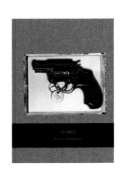

Leutwyler, Henry
Document

€ 65.00 / £ 58.00 / US$ 75.00
ISBN 978-3-86930-969-9

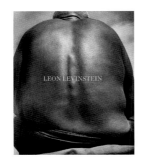

Leon Levinstein

€ 68.00 / £ 58.00 / US$ 85.00
ISBN 978-3-86930-443-4

McMillan, David
Growth and Decay

€ 65.00 / £ 58.00 / US$ 75.00
ISBN 978-3-95829-397-7

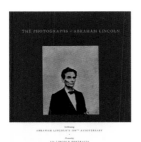

The Photographs of Abraham Lincoln

€ 58.00 / £ 48.00 / US$ 55.00
ISBN 978-3-86930-917-0

Maisel, David
Black Maps

€ 65.00 / £ 55.00 / US$ 85.00
ISBN 978-3-86930-537-0

Lifshitz, Sébastien
Amateur

€ 75.00 / £ 58.00 / US$ 90.00
ISBN 978-3-86930-739-8

Marchand, Yves / Meffre, Romain
Gunkanjima

€ 65.00 / £ 50.00 / US$ 85.00
ISBN 978-3-86930-546-2

Lim, Broy
and now they know

€ 35.00 / £ 30.00 / US$ 40.00
ISBN 978-3-95829-312-0

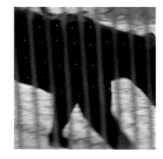

Michener, Diana
A Song of Life

€ 38.00 / £ 35.00 / US$ 40.00
ISBN 978-3-95829-326-7

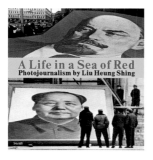

Liu, Heung Shing
A Life in a Sea of Red

€ 85.00 / £ 80.00 / US$ 95.00
ISBN 978-3-95829-545-2

Milella, Domingo

€ 58.00 / £ 48.00 / US$ 55.00
ISBN 978-3-86930-487-8

Löffelbein, Kai
Ctrl-X
A topography of e-waste

€ 38.00 / £ 34.00 / US$ 45.00
ISBN 978-3-86930-970-5

Mocafico, Guido
Mocafico Numéro

€ 145.00 / £ 135.00 / US$ 195.00
ISBN 978-3-86930-907-1

Moffat, Curtis
Silver Society

€ 44.00 / £ 38.00 / US$ 50.00
ISBN 978-3-95829-027-3

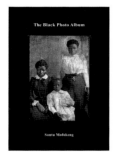

Mofokeng, Santu
The Black Photo Album

€ 34.00 / £ 28.00 / US$ 45.00
ISBN 978-3-86930-310-9

Mofokeng, Santu
Stories 1

€ 28.00 / £ 25.00 / US$ 35.00
ISBN 978-3-86930-971-2

Mofokeng, Santu
Stories 2-4

€ 45.00 / £ 38.00 / US$ 55.00
ISBN 978-3-95829-104-1

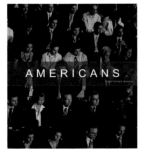

Morris, Christopher
Americans

€ 35.00 / £ 27.00 / US$ 40.00
ISBN 978-3-86930-448-9

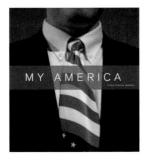

Morris, Christopher
My America

€ 35.00 / £ 27.00 / US$ 40.00
ISBN 978-3-86521-201-6

Martin Munkacsi

€ 65.00 / £ 58.00 / US$ 75.00
ISBN 978-3-86521-269-6

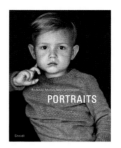

Müller-Westernhagen, Romney
Portraits

€ 42.00 / £ 35.00 / US$ 50.00
ISBN 978-3-86930-817-3

Nádas, Péter
Own Death

€ 40.00 / £ 28.00 / US$ 50.00
ISBN 978-3-86521-010-4

Neville, Mark
Fancy Pictures

€ 48.00 / £ 40.00 / US$ 55.00
ISBN 978-3-86930-908-8

Noguchi, Isamu
A Sculptor's World

€ 58.00 / £ 50.00 / US$ 65.00
ISBN 978-3-86930-915-6

Nozolino, Paulo
bone lonely

€ 34.00 / £ 32.00 / US$ 35.00
ISBN 978-3-86521-861-2

Nozolino, Paulo
Far Cry

€ 45.00 / £ 30.00 / US$ 50.00
ISBN 978-3-86521-122-4

Odermatt, Arnold
Off Duty

€ 65.00 / £ 55.00 / US$ 75.00
ISBN 978-3-86521-796-7

Nozolino, Paulo
Makulatur

€ 25.00 / £ 20.00 / US$ 30.00
ISBN 978-3-86930-327-7

Odermatt, Arnold
After Work

€ 65.00 / £ 55.00 / US$ 75.00
ISBN 978-3-86930-973-6

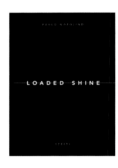

Nozolino, Paulo
Loaded Shine

€ 25.00 / £ 20.00 / US$ 30.00
ISBN 978-3-86930-972-9

Packham, Monte
Concentric Circles

€ 20.00 / £ 17.00 / US$ 27.50
ISBN 978-3-86930-024-5

O'Neal, Hank
A Vision Shared
A Portrait of America 1935-1943

€ 68.00 / £ 60.00 / US$ 75.00
ISBN 978-3-95829-181-2

Pamuk, Orhan
Balkon

€ 34,00 / £ 30.00/ US$ 40.00
ISBN 978-3-95829-399-1

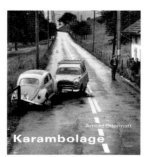

Odermatt, Arnold
Karambolage

€ 65.00 / £ 55.00 / US$ 75.00
ISBN 978-3-88243-866-6

Papageorge, Tod
Dr. Blankman's New York

€ 40.00 / £ 35.00 / US$ 45.00
ISBN 978-3-95829-108-9

Odermatt, Arnold
On Duty

€ 65.00 / £ 55.00 / US$ 75.00
ISBN 978-3-86521-336-5

Park, Jongwoo
DMZ

€ 35.00 / £ 30.00 / US$ 40.00
ISBN 978-3-95829-315-1

Parke, Trent
The Christmas Tree Bucket
Trent Parke's Family Album

€ 38.00 / £ 35.00 / US$ 45.00
ISBN 978-3-86930-206-5

Parks, Gordon
Back to Fort Scott

€ 38.00 / £ 30.00 / US$ 45.00
ISBN 978-3-86930-918-7

Parke, Trent
Minutes to Midnight

€ 38.00 / £ 30.00 / US$ 45.00
ISBN 978-3-86930-205-8

Parks, Gordon
Invisible Man

€ 38.00 / £ 30.00 / US$ 45.00
ISBN 978-3-95829-109-6

Parks, Gordon
A Harlem Family 1967

€ 38.00 / £ 30.00 / US$ 45.00
ISBN 978-3-86930-602-5

Parks, Gordon
The Flavio Story

€ 58.00 / £ 54.00 / US$ 65.00
ISBN 978-3-95829-344-1

Parks, Gordon
The Making of an Argument

€ 38.00 / £ 30.00 / US$ 45.00
ISBN 978-3-86930-721-3

Parks, Gordon
The New Tide, Early Work 1940-1950

€ 58.00 / £ 54.00 / US$ 65.00
ISBN 978-3-95829-488-2

Parks, Gordon
Collected Works

€ 200.00 / £ 180.00 / US$ 225.00
ISBN 978-3-86930-530-1

Parr, Martin (ed.)
The Protest Box

€ 225.00 / £ 185.00 / US$ 250.00
ISBN 978-3-86930-124-2

Parks, Gordon
Collected Works – Study Edition

€ 125.00 / £ 115.00 / US$ 145.00
ISBN 978-3-95829-262-8

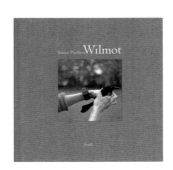

Paulsen, Susan
Wilmot

€ 48.00 / £ 35.00 / US$ 60.00
ISBN 978-3-86930-565-3

Paulsen, Susan
Sarah Ryhmes with Clara

€ 34.00 / £ 40.00 / US$ 50.00
ISBN 978-3-86930-244-7

Peterson, Mark
Political Theatre

€ 35.00 / £ 28.00 / US$ 40.00
ISBN 978-3-95829-183-6

Phillips, Christopher /
Hung, Wu (eds.)
Life and Dreams: Contemporary
Chinese Photography and Media Art

€ 58.00 / £ 55.00 / US$ 60.00
ISBN 978-3-95829-490-5

Polidori, Robert
60 Feet Road

€ 98.00 / £ 88.00 / US$ 125.00
ISBN 978-3-95829-111-9

Polidori, Robert
After the Flood

€ 85.00 / £ 75.00 / US$ 95.00
ISBN 978-3-86521-277-1

Polidori, Robert
Parcours Muséologique Revisité

€ 125.00 / £ 100.00 / US$ 150.00
ISBN 978-3-86521-702-8

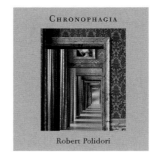

Polidori, Robert
Chronophagia

€ 48.00 / £ 40.00 / US$ 55.00
ISBN 978-3-86930-698-8

Polidori, Robert
Eye and I

€ 48.00 / £ 40.00 / US$ 65.00
ISBN 978-3-86930-592-9

Polidori, Robert
Hotel Petra

€ 48.00 / £ 42.00 / US$ 55.00
ISBN 978-3-95829-184-3

Polidori, Robert
Topographical Histories

€ 35,00 / £ 30.00 / US$ 50.00
ISBN 978-3-95829-549-0

Polidori, Robert
Synchrony and Diachrony
Photographs of the J. P. Getty
Museum 1997

€ 38.00 / £ 35.00 / US$ 45.00
ISBN 978-3-95829-383-0

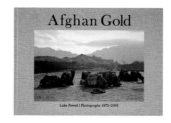

Powell, Luke
Afghan Gold

€ 98.00 / £ 95.00 / US$ 125.00
ISBN 978-3-86930-648-3

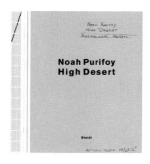

Purifoy, Noah
High Desert

€ 40.00 / £ 38.00 / US$ 60.00
ISBN 978-3-86930-595-0

Rautert, Timm
No Photographing

€ 38.00 / £ 32.00 / US$ 45.00
ISBN 978-3-86930-322-2

Rautert, Timm
Josef Sudek, Prague 1967

€ 40.00 / £ 35.00 / US$ 50.00
ISBN 978-3-95829-118-8

Rautert, Timm
Germans in Uniform

€ 34.00 / £ 30.00 / US$ 45.00
ISBN 978-3-95829-287-1

Rautert, Timm
Anfang / Beginnings

€ 58.00 / £ 70.00 / US$ 75.00
ISBN 978-3-95829-528-5

Renhui, Robert Zhao
A Guide to the Flora and Fauna

€ 58.00 / £ 55.00 / US$ 60.00
ISBN 978-3-95829-319-9

Riddy, John
Photographs

€ 75.00 / £ 70.00 / US$ 85.00
ISBN 978-3-95829-566-7

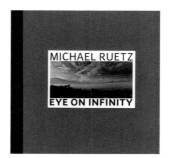

Ruetz, Michael
Eye on Infinity

€ 48.00 / £ 45.00 / US$ 55.00
ISBN 978-3-86521-766-0

Ruetz, Michael
The Family of Dog

€ 38.00 / £ 30.00 / US$ 45.00
ISBN 978-3-86930-575-2

Ruetz, Michael
Eye on Time

€ 48.00 / £ 45.00 / US$ 55.00
ISBN 978-3-86521-577-2

Ruscha, Ed
THEN & NOW

€ 195.00 / £ 185.00 / US$ 250.00
ISBN 978-3-86521-105-7

Ruscha, Ed
Catalogue Raisonné of the
Paintings, Volume 1: 1958-1970

€ 165.00 / £ 155.00 / US$ 200.00
ISBN 978-3-88243-972-4

Ruscha, Ed
Catalogue Raisonné of the
Paintings, Volume 2: 1971–1982

€ 165.00 / £ 155.00 / US$ 200.00
ISBN 978-3-86521-138-5

Ruscha, Ed
Catalogue Raisonné of the
Paintings, Volume 3: 1983–1987

€ 165.00 / £ 155.00 / US$ 200.00
ISBN 978-3-86521-368-6

Ruscha, Ed
Catalogue Raisonné of the
Paintings, Volume 4: 1988–1992

€ 165.00 / £ 155.00 / US$ 200.00
ISBN 978-3-86521-833-9

Ruscha, Ed
Catalogue Raisonné of the
Paintings, Volume 5: 1993–1997

€ 165.00 / £ 155.00 / US$ 200.00
ISBN 978-3-86930-251-5

Ruscha, Ed
Catalogue Raisonné of the
Paintings, Volume 6: 1998–2003

€ 165.00 / £ 155.00 / US$ 200.00
ISBN 978-3-86930-740-4

Ruscha, Ed
Catalogue Raisonné of the
Paintings. Volume 7: 2004–2011

€ 165.00 / £ 155.00 / US$ 200.00
ISBN 978-3-95829-186-7

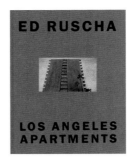

Ruscha, Ed
Los Angeles Apartments

€ 38.00 / £ 30.00 / US$ 45.00
ISBN 978-3-869630-596-7

Ryan, Liza
The Unreal Real

€ 38,00 / £ 35.00 / US$ 45.00
ISBN 978-3-95829-351-9

Sander, August
Persecuted/Persecutors
People of the 20th Century

€ 30.00 / £ 27.00 / US$ 40.00
ISBN 978-3-95829-511-7

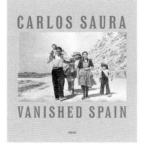

Saura, Carlos
Vanished Spain

€ 65.00 / £ 58.00 / US$ 80.00
ISBN 978-3-86930-911-8

Savulich, Andrew
The City

€ 38.00 / £ 30.00 / US$ 45.00
ISBN 978-3-86930-690-2

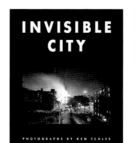

Schles, Ken
Invisible City

€ 34.00 / £ 28.00 / US$ 40.00
ISBN 978-3-86930-691-9

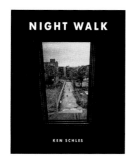

Schles, Ken
Night Walk

€ 38.00 / £ 30.00 / US$ 45.00
ISBN 978-3-86930-692-6

Schmidt, Jason
Artists II

€ 58.00 / £ 48.00 / US$ 70.00
ISBN 978-3-86930-632-2

Schulze / Ruelfs (eds.)
ReVision

€ 48.00 / £ 45.00 / US$ 58.00
ISBN 978-3-95829-185-0

Schwartzwald, Lawrence
The Art of Reading

€ 28.00 / £ 25.00 / US$ 30.00
ISBN 978-3-95829-508-7

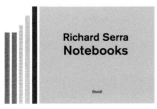

Serra, Richard
Notebooks, Vol. 1

€ 380.00 / £ 325.00 / US$ 400.00
ISBN 978-3-86930-253-9

Serra, Richard
Forged Steel

€ 38.00 / £ 32.00
ISBN 978-3-95829-188-1
[Distributed in the USA by David
Zwirner (D.A.P.)]

Serra, Richard
Vertical and Horizontal Reversals

€ 58.00 / £ 52.00
ISBN 978-3-86930-978-1
[Distributed in the USA by David
Zwirner (D.A.P.)]

Serra, Richard
Early Work

€ 68.00 / £ 54.00 / US$ 85.00
ISBN 978-3-86930-716-9

Swecz, Maria
inter esse

€ 38.00 / £ 30.00 / US$ 45.00
ISBN 978-3-86521-788-2

Sheikh, Fazal
Portraits

€ 48.00 / £ 42.00 / US$ 55.00
ISBN 978-3-86521-819-3

Sheikh, Fazal
Moksha

€ 65.00 / £ 55.00 / US$ 70.00
ISBN 978-3-86521-125-5

Sheikh, Fazal
The Circle

€ 30.00 / £ 20.00 / US$ 40.00
ISBN 978-3-86521-599-4

Sheikh, Fazal
Ether

€ 38.00 / £ 30.00 / US$ 45.00
ISBN 978-3-86930-653-7

Sheikh, Fazal
The Erasure Trilogy

€ 98.00 / £ 85.00 / US$ 125.00
ISBN 978-3-86930-805-0

Singh, Dayanita
Museum of Chance

€ 48.00 / £ 40.00 / US$ 55.00
ISBN 978-3-86930-693-3

Singh, Dayanita
Dream Villa

€ 28.00 / £ 24.00 / US$ 35.00
ISBN 978-3-86521-985-5

Sory, Sanlé
Volta Photo

€ 38.00 / £ 35.00 / US$ 40.00
ISBN 978-3-95829-400-4

Staeck, Klaus / Steidl, Gerhard
Beuys Book

€ 45.00 / £ 40.00 / US$ 50.00
ISBN 978-3-86521-914-5

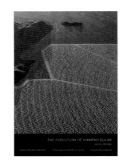

Stillings, Jamey
The Evolution of Ivanpah Solar

€ 65.00 / £ 58.00 / US$ 70.00
ISBN 978-3-86930-913-2

Sternfeld, Joel
On This Site

€ 48.00 / £ 42.00 / US$ 55.00
ISBN 978-3-86930-434-2

Sternfeld, Joel
First Pictures

€ 48.00 / £ 42.00 / US$ 55.00
ISBN 978-3-86930-309-3

Sternfeld, Joel
iDubai

€ 28.00 / £ 24.00 / US$ 30.00
ISBN 978-3-86521-916-9

Sternfeld, Joel
When it Changed

€ 25.00 / £ 20.00 / US$ 30.00
ISBN 978-3-86521-278-8

Sternfeld, Joel
Stranger Passing

€ 65.00 / £ 50.00 / US$ 75.00
ISBN 978-3-86930-499-1

Sturges, Jock
Fanny

€ 78.00 / £ 65.00 / US$ 90.00
ISBN 978-3-86930-694-0

Teller, Juergen
Nürnberg

€ 75.00 / £ 65.00 / US$ 80.00
ISBN 978-3-86521-132-3

Subotzky, Mikhael
Retinal Shift

€ 38.00 / £ 30.00 / US$ 45.00
ISBN 978-3-86930-539-4

Teller, Juergen
The Keys to the House

€ 45.00 / £ 39.00 / US$ 50.00
ISBN 978-3-86930-383-3

Sutkus, Antanas
Planet Lithuania

€ 38.00 / £ 40.00 / US$ 45.00
ISBN 978-3-95829-512-4

Teller, Juergen
Woo!

€ 40.00 / £ 30.00 / US$ 45.00
ISBN 978-3-86930-652-0

Taylor-Johnson, Sam
Birth of a Clown

€ 34.00 / £ 28.00 / US$ 40.00
ISBN 978-3-86521-853-7

Teller, Juergen
Siegerflieger

€ 29.80 / £ 25.00 / US$ 35.00
ISBN 978-3-86930-914-9

Taylor-Johnson, Sam
Second Floor

€ 50.00 / £ 45.00 / US$ 60.00
ISBN 978-3-86930-264-5

Teller, Juergen
Märchenstüberl

€ 22.00 / £ 14.00 / US$ 30.00
ISBN 978-3-88243-863-5

Teller, Juergen
Nackig auf dem Fußballplatz

€ 25.00 / £ 18.00 / US$ 30.00
ISBN 978-3-88243-963-2

Teller, Juergen
The Master IV

€ 15.00 / £ 10.00 / US$ 20.00
ISBN 978-3-95829-575-9

Tillim, Guy
O Futuro Certo

€ 45.00 / £ 40.00 / US$ 50.00
ISBN 978-3-86930-649-0

Trager, Philip
Photographing Ina

€ 38.00 / £ 34.00 / US$ 45.00
ISBN 978-3-86930-977-4

Trager, Philip
New York in the 1970s

€ 48.00 / £ 40.00 / US$ 55.00
ISBN 978-3-86930-806-7

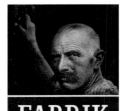

Tuggener, Jakob
Fabrik

€ 65.00 / £ 55.00 / US$ 75.00
ISBN 978-3-86521-493-5

Tuggener, Jakob
Books and Films

€ 700.00 / £ 650.00 / US$ 800.00
ISBN 978-3-95829-328-1

Verzosa, Jake
The Last Tattooed Women of Kalinga

€ 35.00 / £ 30.00 / US$ 40.00
ISBN 978-3-95829-317-5

Voit, Robert
New Trees

€ 58.00 / £ 45.00 / US$ 65.00
ISBN 978-3-86521-825-4

Wallis, Brian (ed.)
The Order of Things

€ 85.00 / £ 78.00 / US$ 95.00
ISBN 978-3-86930-994-1

Weinberger, Karlheinz
Swiss Rebels

€ 65.00 / £ 58.00 / US$ 68.00
ISBN 978-3-95829-329-8

Wessel, Henry
Waikiki

€ 58.00 / £ 50.00 / US$ 65.00
ISBN 978-3-89630-300-0

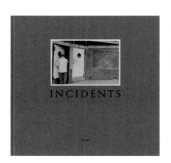

Wessel, Henry
Incidents

€ 58.00 / £ 50.00 / US$ 65.00
ISBN 978-3-86930-697-1

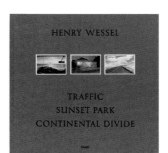

Wessel, Henry
Traffic / Sunset Park /
Continental Divide

€ 75.00 / £ 70.00 / US$ 85.00
ISBN 978-3-95829-275-8

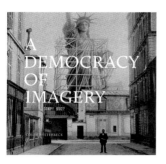

Westerbeck, Colin
A Democracy of Imagery

€ 45.00 / £ 40.00 / US$ 50.00
ISBN 978-3-95829-116-4

Wood, Tom
Men and Women

€ 68.00 / £ 58.00 / US$ 70.00
ISBN 978-3-86930-570-7

Wettre, Jonas
Once There were Polaroids

€ 30.00 / £ 25.00 / US$ 35.00
ISBN 978-3-86930-963-7

Soak Teng, Woong
Ways to Tie Trees

€ 50.00 / £ 45.00 / US$ 55.00
ISBN 978-3-95829-316-8

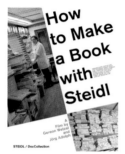

Wetzel, Gereon / Adolph, Jörg
How to Make a Book with Steidl

€ 15.00 / £ 12.00 / US$ 20.00
ISBN 978-3-86930-119-8

Wylie, Donovan
Housing Plans for the Future

€ 35.00 / £ 30.00 / US$ 40.00
ISBN 978-3-95829-488-2

Wetzel, Gereon / Adolph, Jörg
How to Make a Book with Carlos
Saura & Steidl

€ 15.00 / £ 12.00 / US$ 20.00
ISBN 978-3-95829-353-3

Whyte-Ball, Ken and Victoria (eds.)
The Golden Decade

€ 58.00 / £ 50.00 / US$ 65.00
ISBN 978-3-86930-902-6

Wiedenhöfer, Kai
Confrontier

€ 40.00 / £ 32.00 / US$ 45.00
ISBN 978-3-86930-550-9

Zimmermann, Harf
Brand Wand

€ 78.00 / £ 65.00 / US$ 90.00
ISBN 978-3-86930-628-5

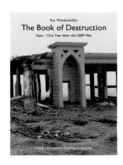

Wiedenhöfer, Kai
The Book of Destruction

€ 34.00 / £ 30.00 / US$ 40.00
ISBN 978-3-86930-207-2

steidl.de